Transparency Masters

to accompany

Technical Graphics Communication

Second Edition

Gary R. Bertoline

Eric N. Wiebe

Craig L. Miller

James L. Mohler

Boston   Burr Ridge, IL   Dubuque, IA   Madison, WI   New York   San Francisco   St. Louis
Bangkok   Bogotá   Caracas   Lisbon   London   Madrid
Mexico City   Milan   New Delhi   Seoul   Singapore   Sydney   Taipei   Toronto

WCB/McGraw-Hill

A Division of The McGraw-Hill Companies

Transparency Masters to accompany
TECHNICAL GRAPHICS COMMUNICATION

2 3 4 5 6 7 8 9 0 MAZ/MAZ 9 0 9 8 7

ISBN 0-256-26343-4

http://www.mhhe.com

TM-1 Figure 1.5
Users of Graphics

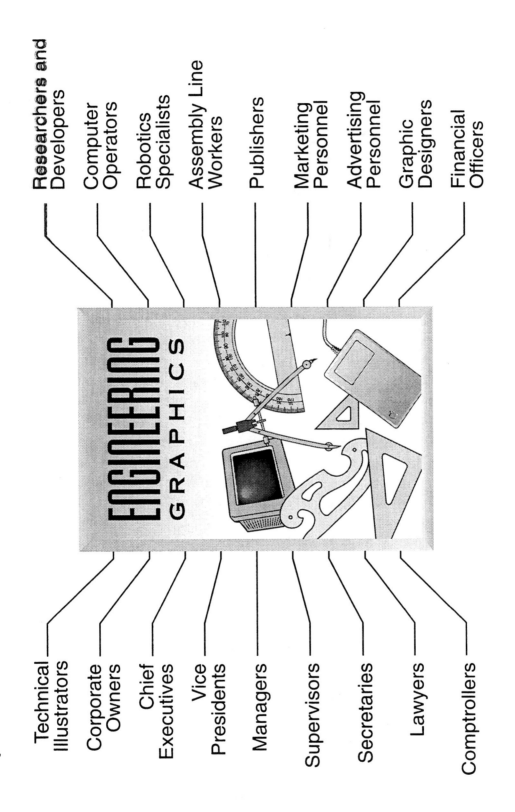

Researchers and Developers

Computer Operators

Robotics Specialists

Assembly Line Workers

Publishers

Marketing Personnel

Advertising Personnel

Graphic Designers

Financial Officers

Technical Illustrators

Corporate Owners

Chief Executives

Vice Presidents

Managers

Supervisors

Secretaries

Lawyers

Comptrollers

ENGINEERING GRAPHICS

TM-2   Figure 1.11
Historical Timeline of Major Events in Graphics over the Last Four Millennia

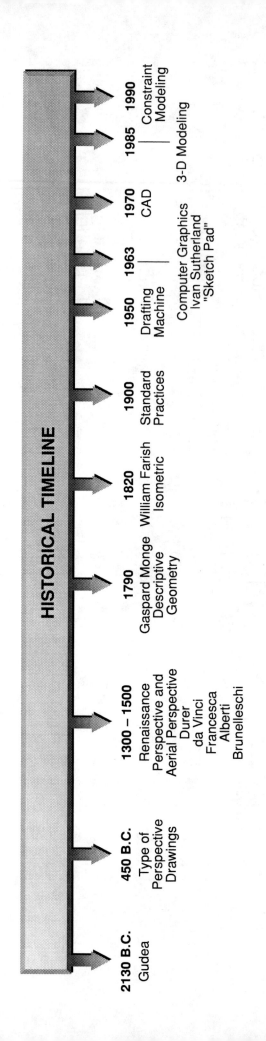

TM-3   Figure 1.17
Linear Engineering Design Process

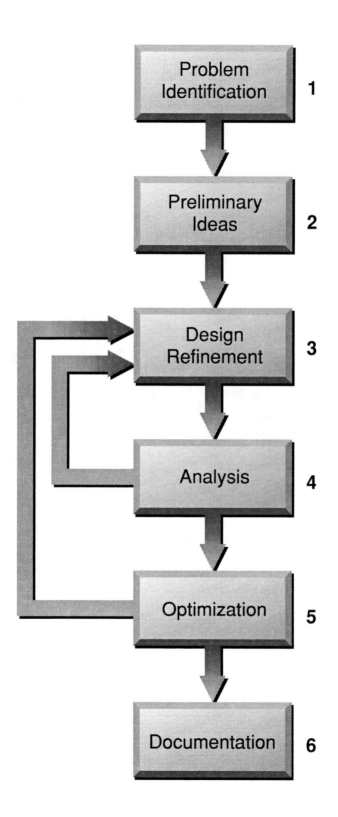

TM-4   Figure 1.20
Concurrent Engineering Design Process

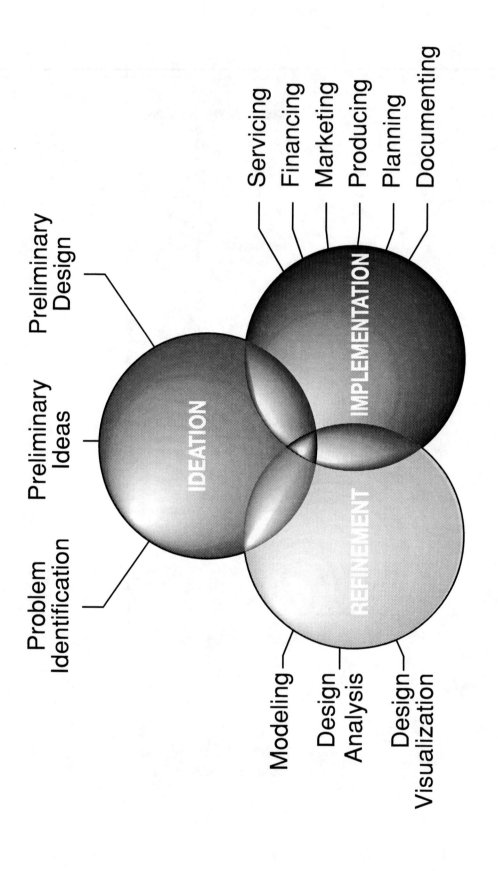

TM-5   Figure 1.21
CAD Database Applications

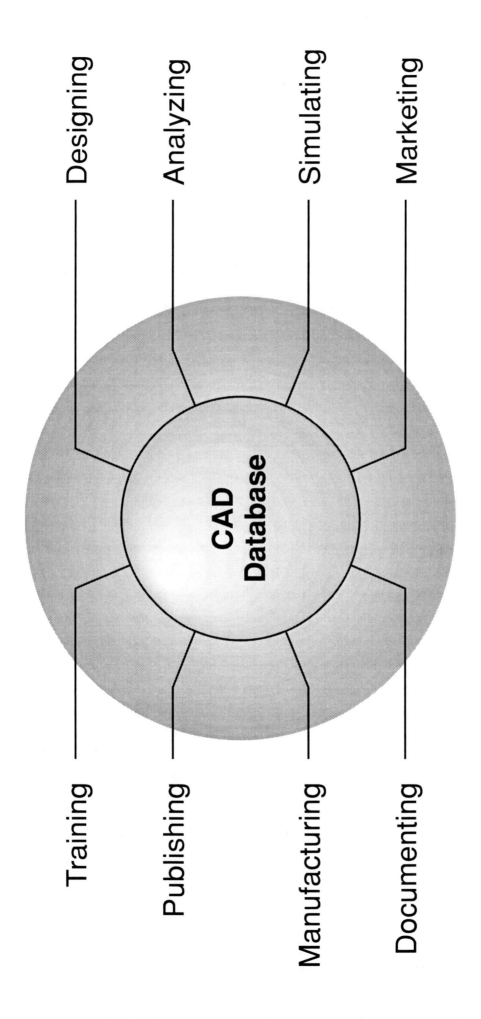

Designing

Analyzing

Simulating

Marketing

Training

Publishing

Manufacturing

Documenting

**CAD
Database**

TM-6 Figure 1.22
Visual Science

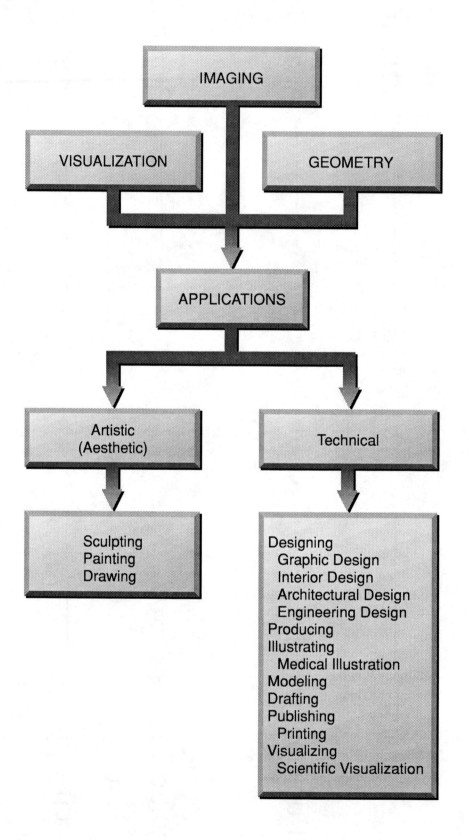

TM-7   Figure 1.26
Standards and Conventional Practices

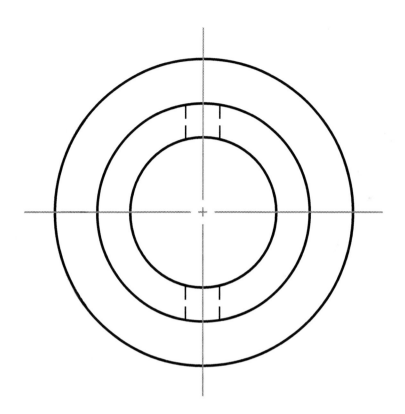

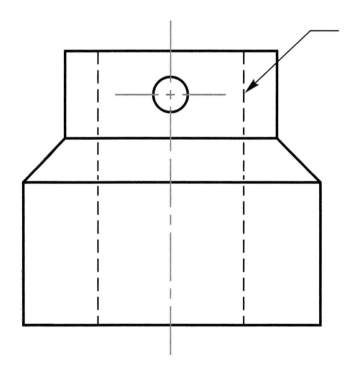

Dashed lines are an
example of a drawing
convention

TM-8 Figure 1.27
Dimensioned Mechanical Drawing Using ASME Y14.1M–1994 Standards

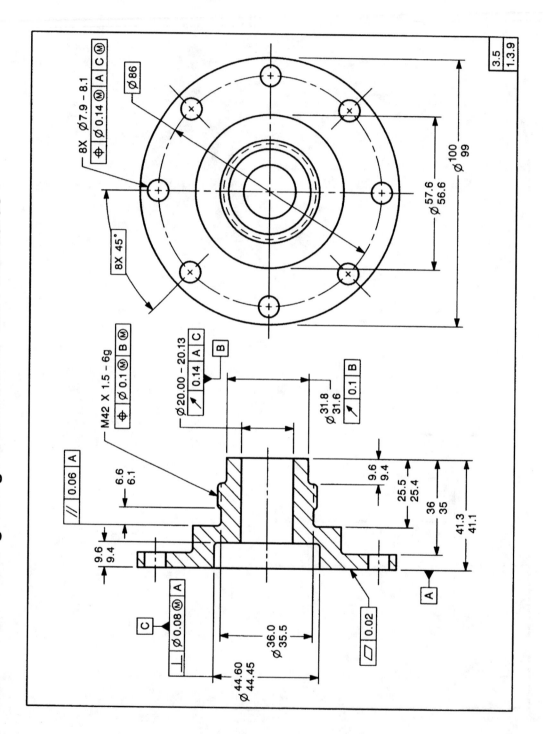

TM-9
Figure 1.29
Problem 1.6 Bearing Block to Be Described Verbally

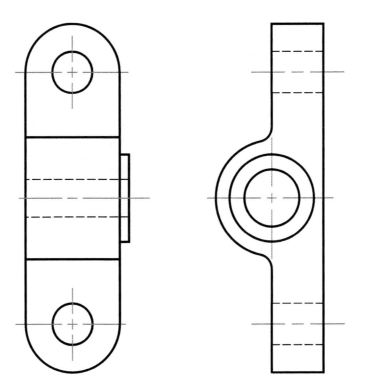

TM-10   Figure 2.1
Design Is Grouped as Artistic and Technical

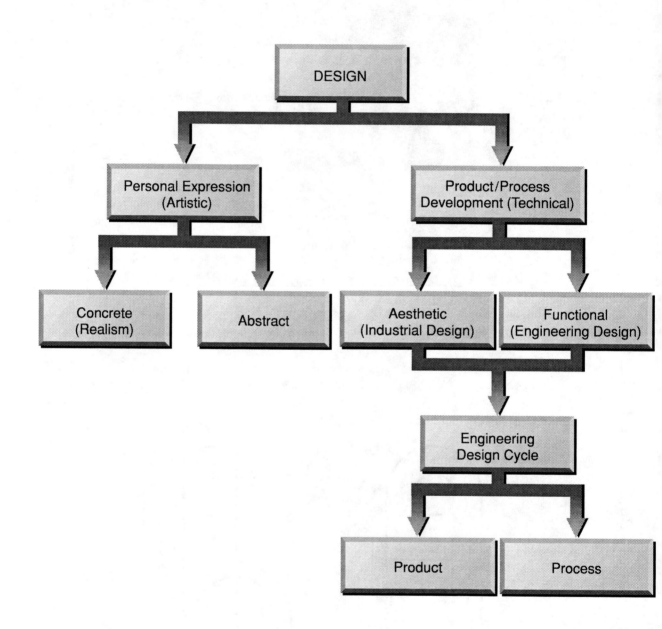

TM-11 Figure 2.7
Sharing the CAD Database

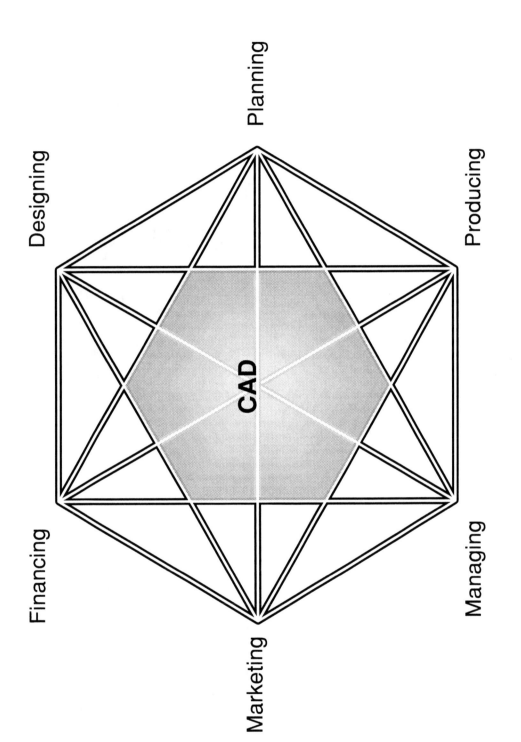

Planning

Producing

Managing

Marketing

Financing

Designing

CAD

TM-12 Figure 2.8
Concurrent Engineering Design

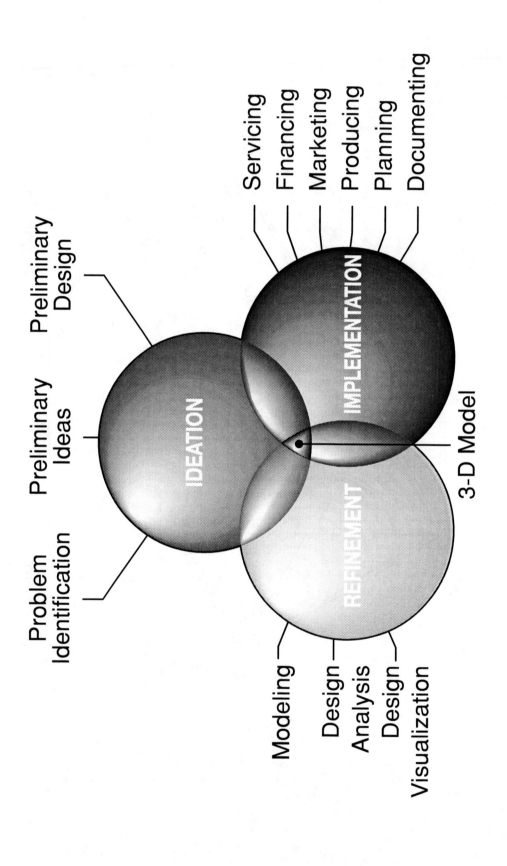

TM-13
Figure 2.10
Ideation Process

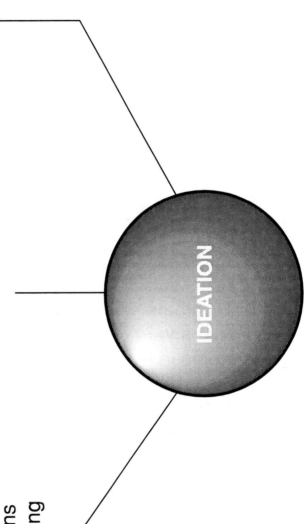

**Problem
Identification**

- Problem Statement
- Research
- Data Gathering
- Objectives
- Limitations
- Scheduling

**Preliminary
Ideas**

- Notes
- Sketches/Models
- Brainstorm
- Synthesis

**Preliminary
Design**

- Evaluation
- Selection

IDEATION

TM-14   Figure 2.16
Refinement Process

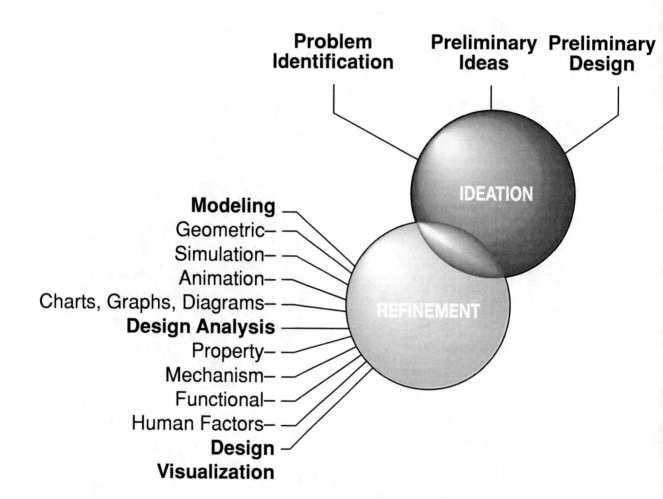

Problem Identification

Preliminary Ideas

Preliminary Design

IDEATION

Modeling
Geometric–
Simulation–
Animation–
Charts, Graphs, Diagrams–
Design Analysis
Property–
Mechanism–
Functional–
Human Factors–
Design
Visualization

REFINEMENT

TM-15 Figure 2.39
Implementation Process

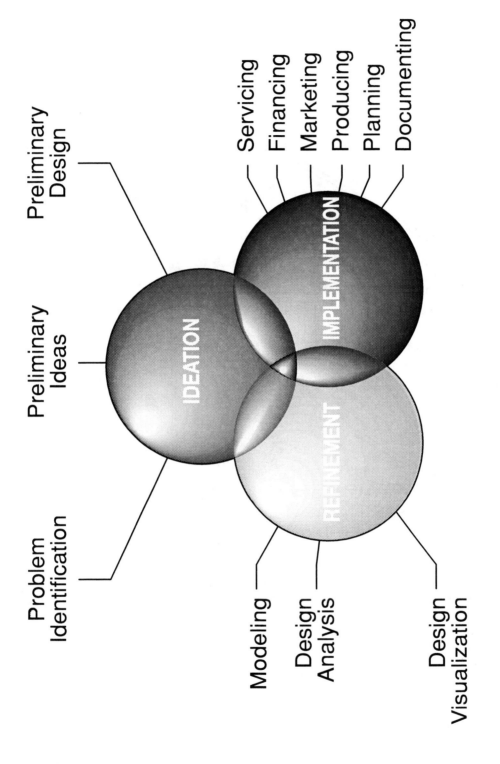

Preliminary Design

Preliminary Ideas

Problem Identification

IDEATION

IMPLEMENTATION

REFINEMENT

Servicing
Financing
Marketing
Producing
Planning
Documenting

Modeling
Design Analysis
Design Visualization

TM-16   Figure 2.52
Concurrent Documentation

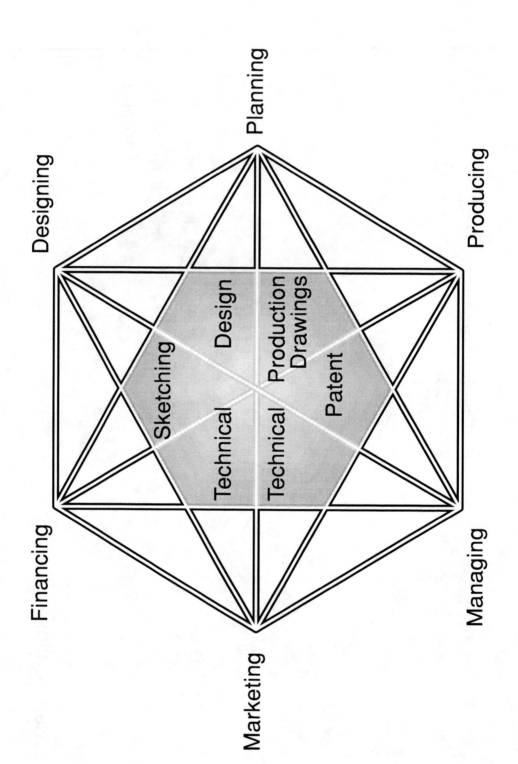

Individual Workstations

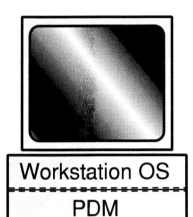

Workstation OS

PDM

Workstation OS

PDM Client Software

Workstation OS

PDM Client Software

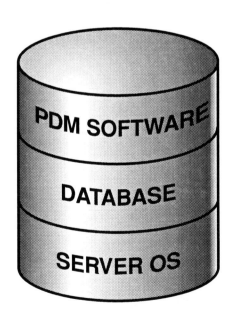

PDM SOFTWARE

DATABASE

SERVER OS

Network Server

An Exploded Assembly Drawing of the Gear Reducer

ITEM	QTY	NAME	DESCRIPTION
1	1	HOUSING	CAST IRON
2	2	TAPER PLUG	.500-16NPT
3	2	RETAINING PLATE	CAST IRON
4	1	SLOW SPEED SHAFT	SAE 4340
5	1	WORM GEAR	BRONZE
6	1	MOTOR ADAPTOR	CAST IRON
7	1	HIGH SPEED OIL SEAL	
8	4	HEX HEAD CAP SCREW	7/16-14UNC-2A X 2.25
9	8	HEX HEAD CAP SCREW	1/2-13UNC-2A X .75
10	2	SLOW SPEED OIL SEAL	
11	1	SLOW SPEED KEYWAY	1/4 X 1/4 X 1.75
12	2	SNGL. ROW TAPER ROLLER BEARING	(NTN) 4T-LM67048
13	2	SLOW SPEED SPACER	SAE 1060
14	1	SNGL. ROW CYLINDER BEARING	(NTN) N10/NU10 #1008
15	1	HIGH SPEED SHAFT	SAE 4140
16	1	BEARING CAP	
17	4	HEX HEAD CAP SCREW	7/16-14UNC-2A X 2.75
18	1	HEX NUT	1-8UN-2B
19	2	HIGH SPEED LOCKWASHER	
20	2	DBLE. ROW TAPERED ROLLER BEARING	(NTN) 4T-2690
21	2	INTERNAL RETAINING RING	SAE 1060

TM-19 Figure 3.36
Line Weight

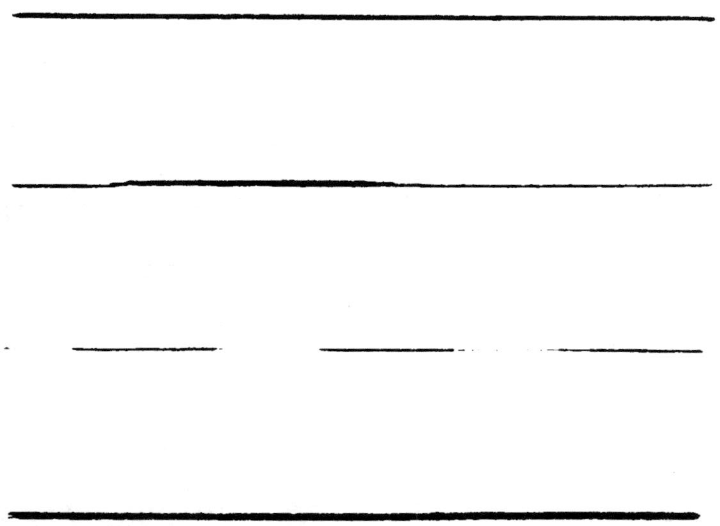

.5MM GOOD TECHNIQUE

.5MM POOR- LINE THICKNESS VARIES

.5MM POOR- DARKNESS VARIES

.7MM GOOD TECHNIQUE

TM-20   Figure 3.37
Pencil Grades

HARD

The hard leads are used for construction

MEDIUM

The medium grades are used for general use on technical drawings. The harder grades are for instrument drawings and the softer

SOFT

Soft leads are used for technical sketching and artwork but are too soft for instrument

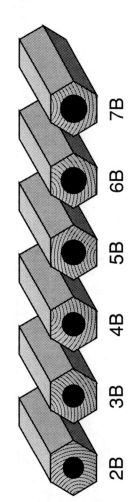

9H 8H 7H 6H 5H 4H

3H 2H H F HB B

2B 3B 4B 5B 6B 7B

TM-21   Table 3.2
ANSI Standard Sheet Sizes

Metric (mm)	U.S. Standard	Architectural
A4 210 × 297	A-Size 8.5" × 11"	9" × 12"
A3 297 × 412	B-Size 11" × 17"	12" × 18"
A2 420 × 524	C-Size 17" × 22"	18" × 24"
A1 594 × 841	D-Size 22" × 34"	24" × 36"
A0 841 × 1189	E-Size 34" × 44"	36" × 48"

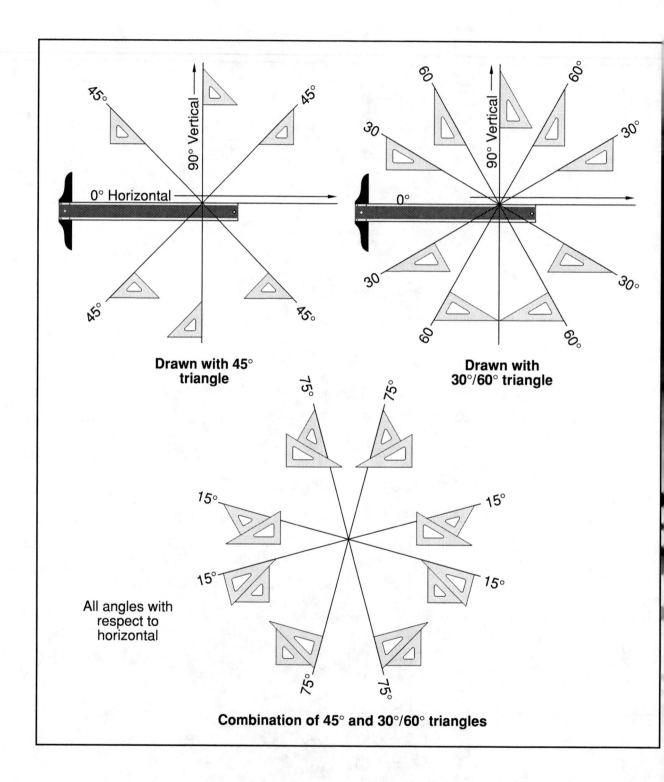

Drawn with 45°
triangle

Drawn with
30°/60° triangle

All angles with
respect to
horizontal

Combination of 45° and 30°/60° triangles

TM-23 Figure 3.41
The Alphabet of Lines

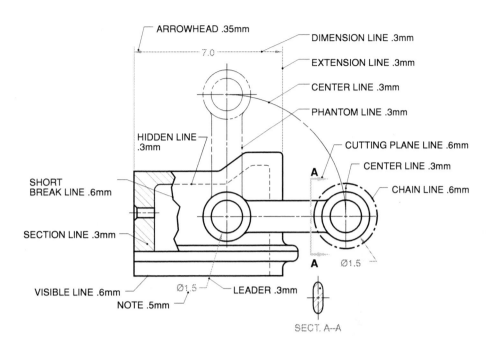

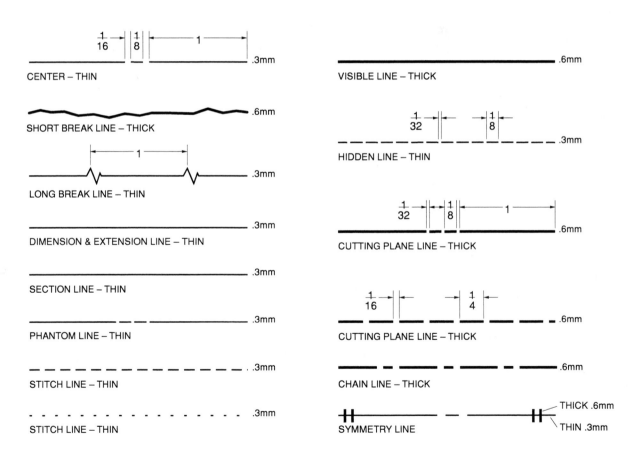

TM-24 Figure 3.42
AutoCAD's Linestyle Menu Showing Some of the Linetypes Available

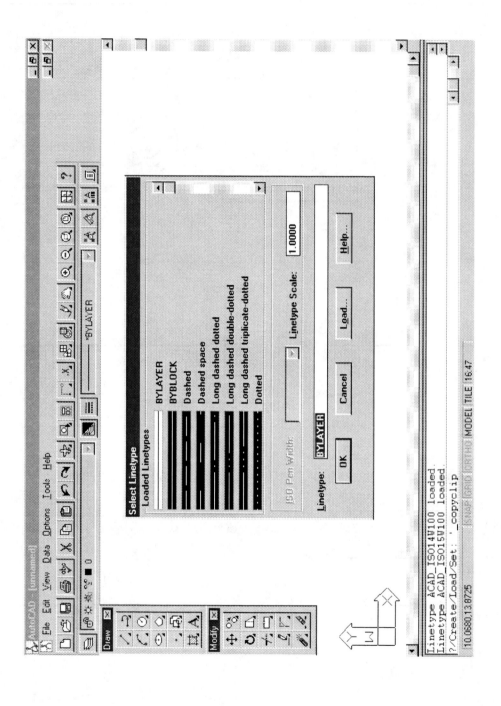

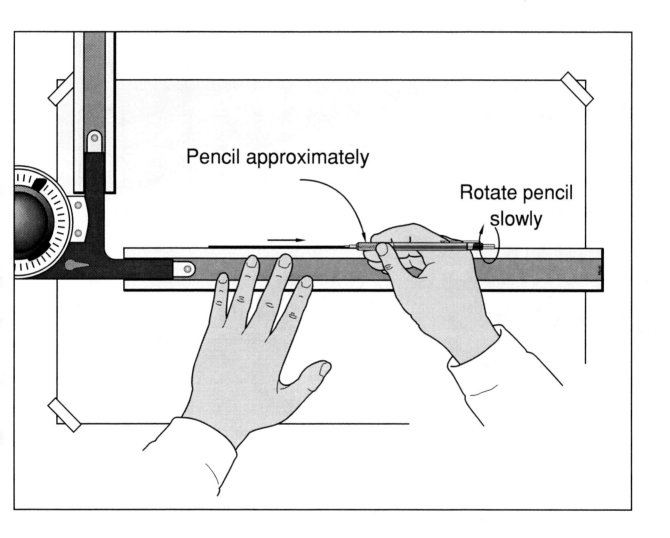

Pencil approximately

Rotate pencil slowly

TM-26   Figure 3.44
Drawing Vertical Lines

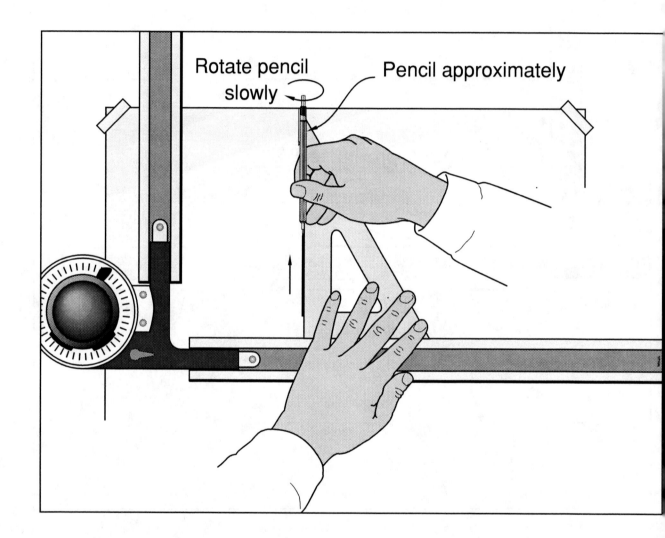

Rotate pencil slowly

Pencil approximately

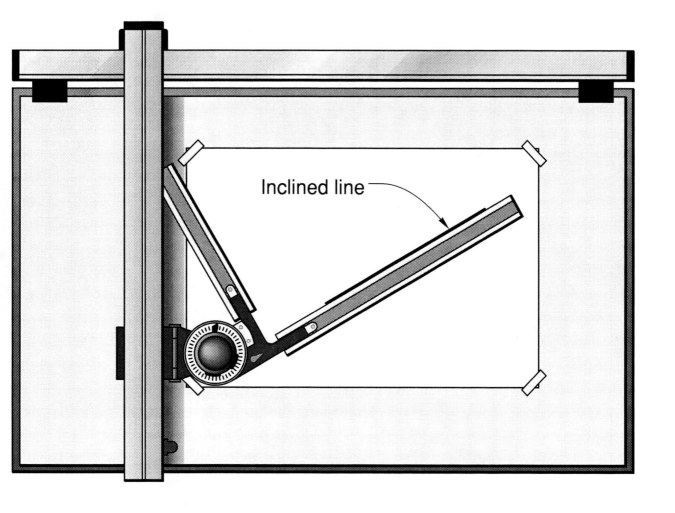

Inclined line

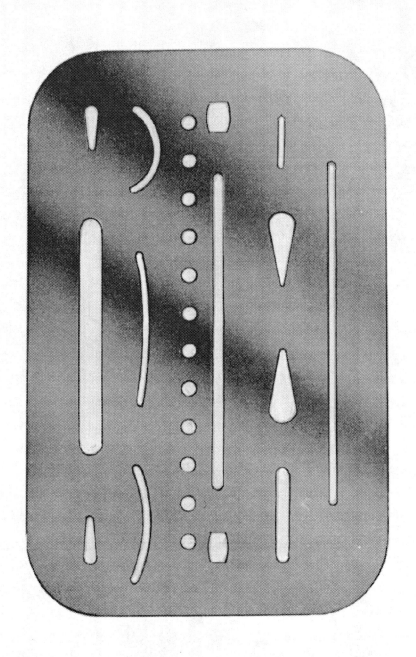

TM-29   Figure 3.47
Drawing a Line through Two Points

Edge of triangle
aligned with the
points

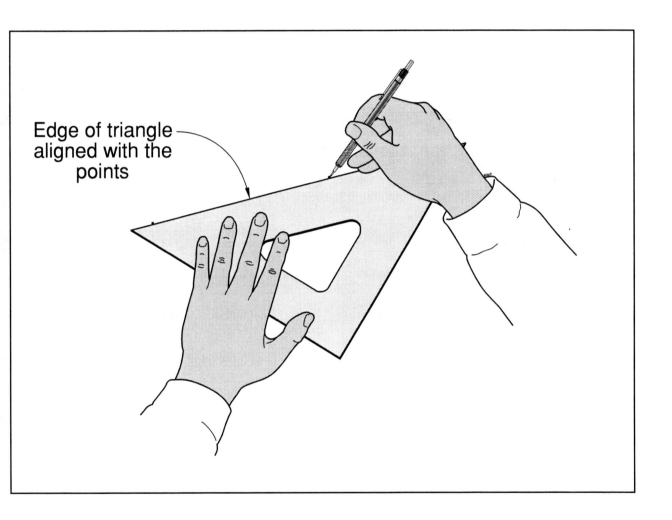

TM-30 Figure 3.48
Drawing Parallel Lines

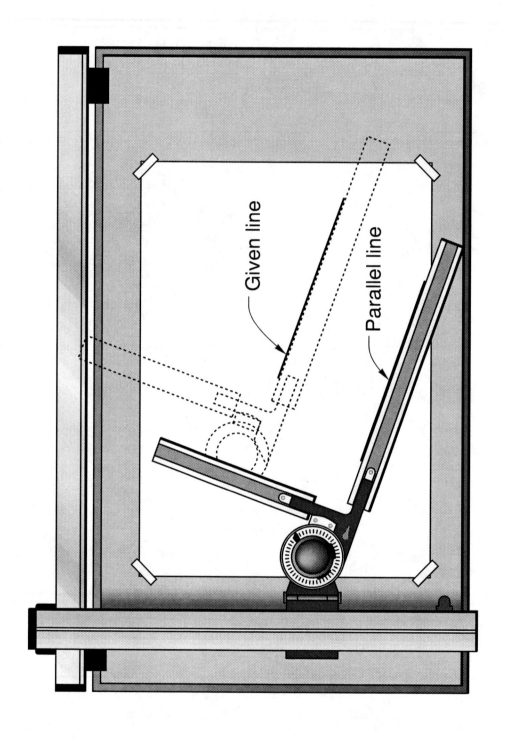

Given line

Parallel line

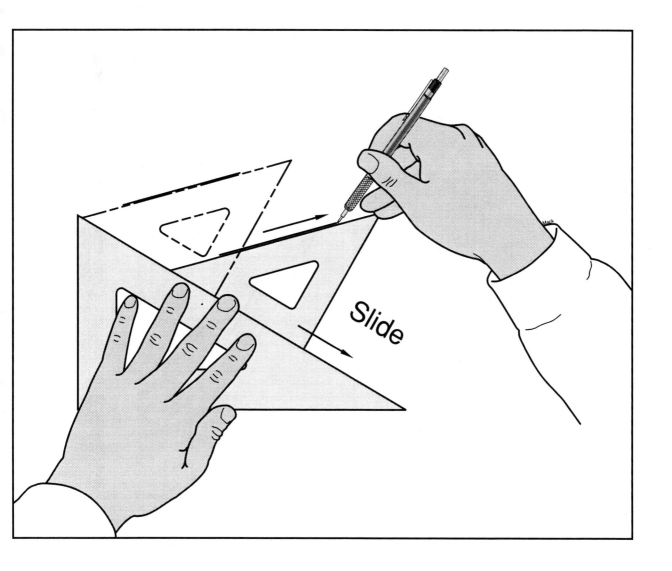

Slide

TM-32   Figure 3.50
Drawing Perpendicular Lines

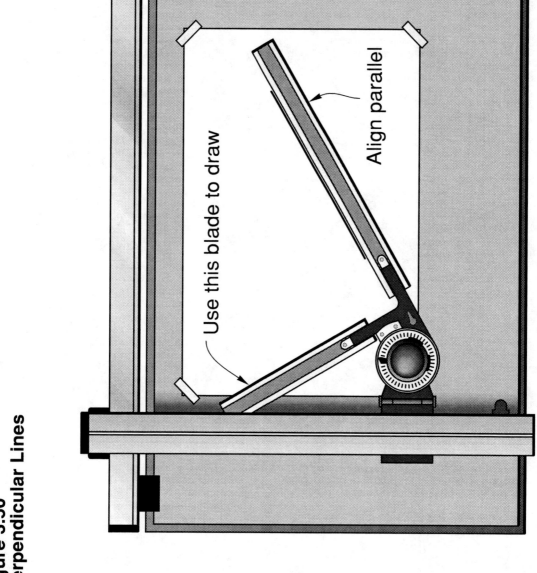

Use this blade to draw

Align parallel

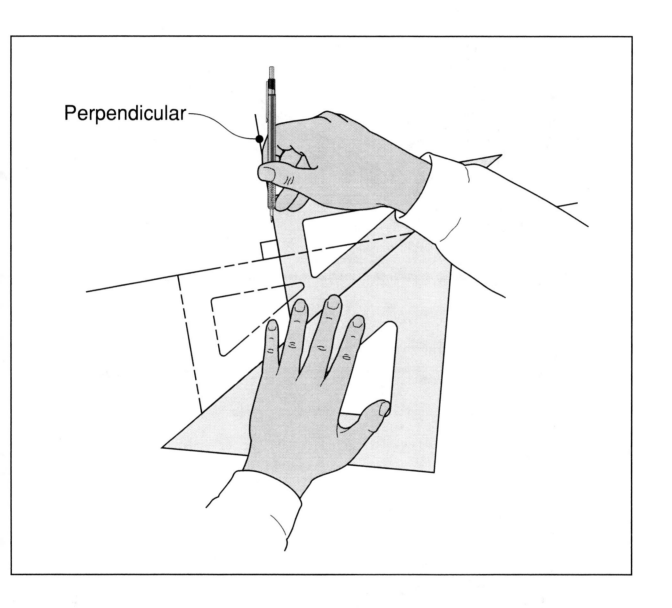

Perpendicular

TM-34 Figure 3.52
Drawing a Line at an Angle

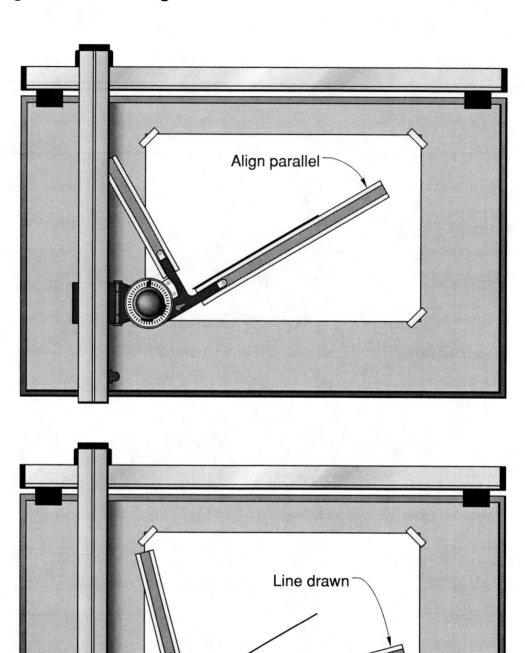

Align parallel

Line drawn

Angle relative to given line

Drawing a Line at an Angle Using Two Triangles

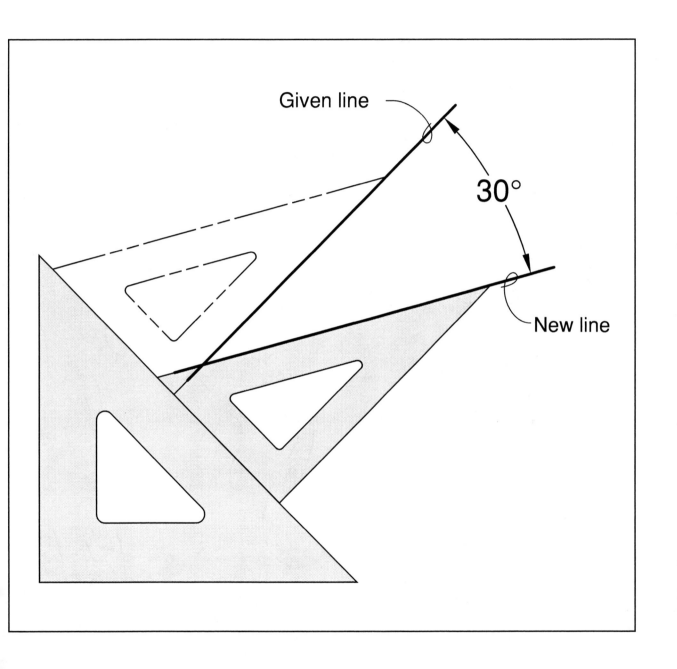

Given line

30°

New line

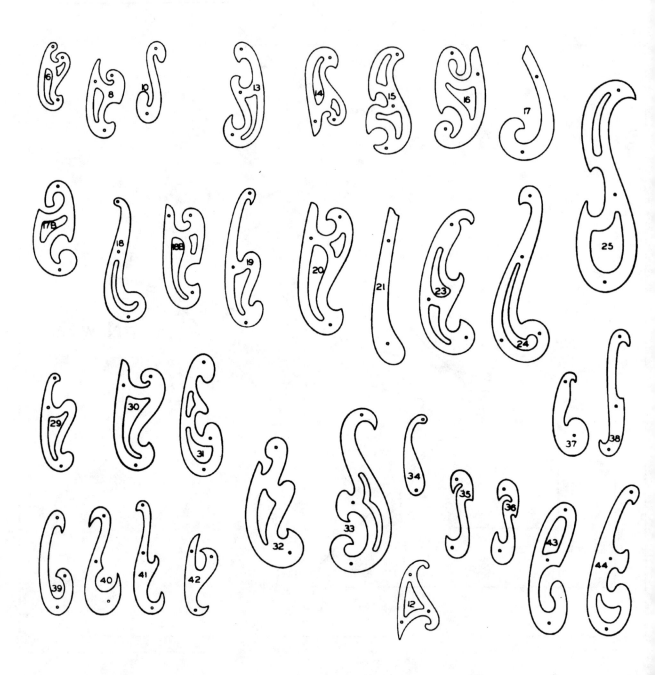

The McGraw-Hill Companies, Inc., 1997

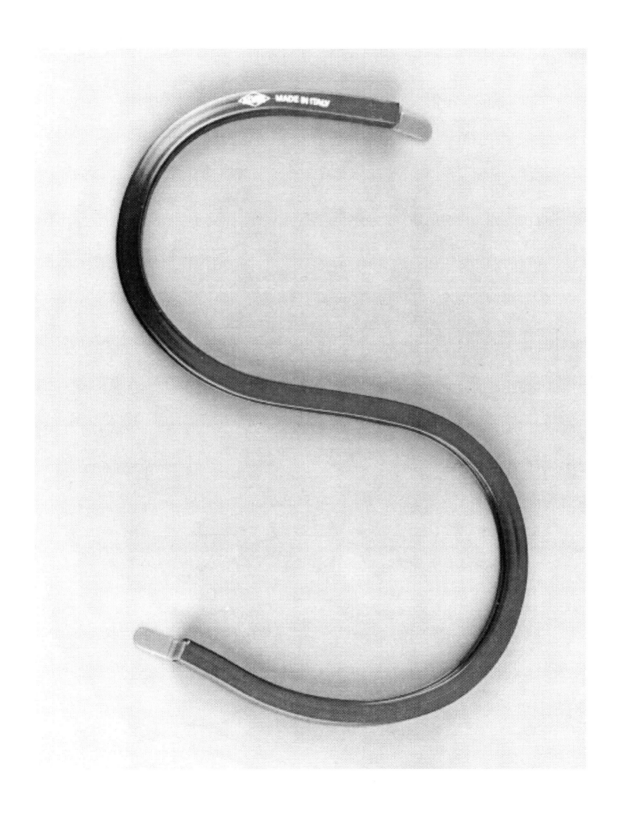

Courtesy of Alvin & Company.

TM-38   Figure 3.56
Steps in Drawing an Irregular Curve through a Series of Points

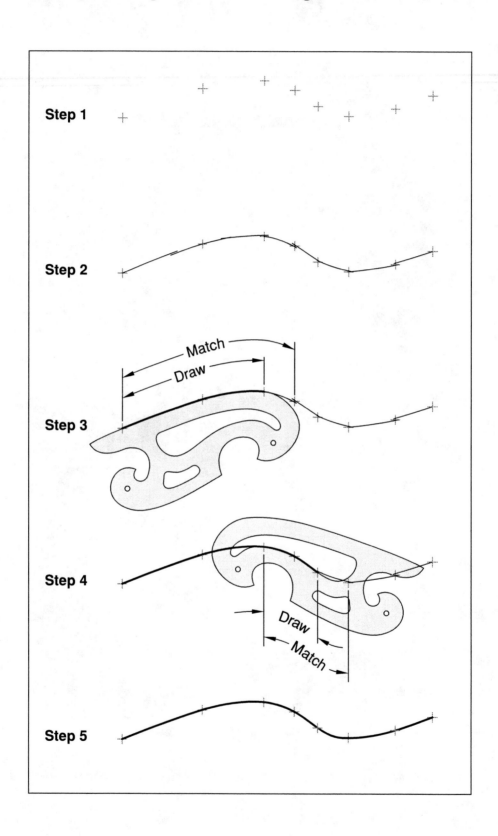

TM-39   Figure 3.57
Architect's Scale

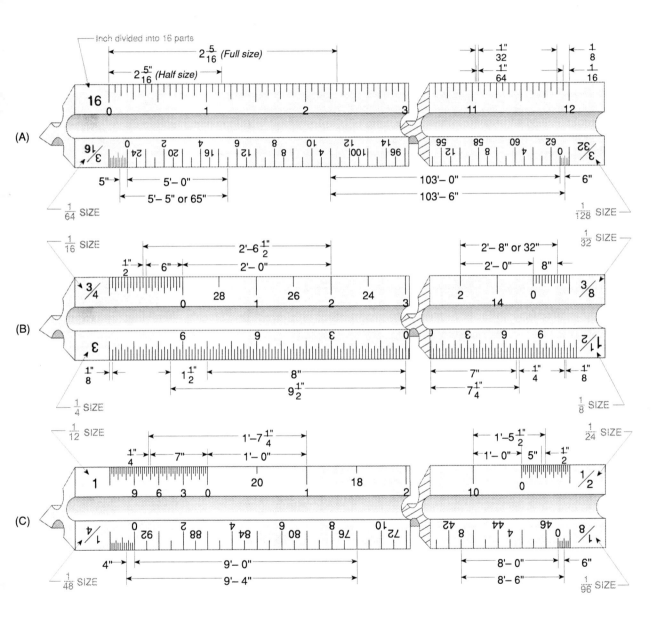

TM-40   Figure 3.58
Steps in Reading an Architect's Scale

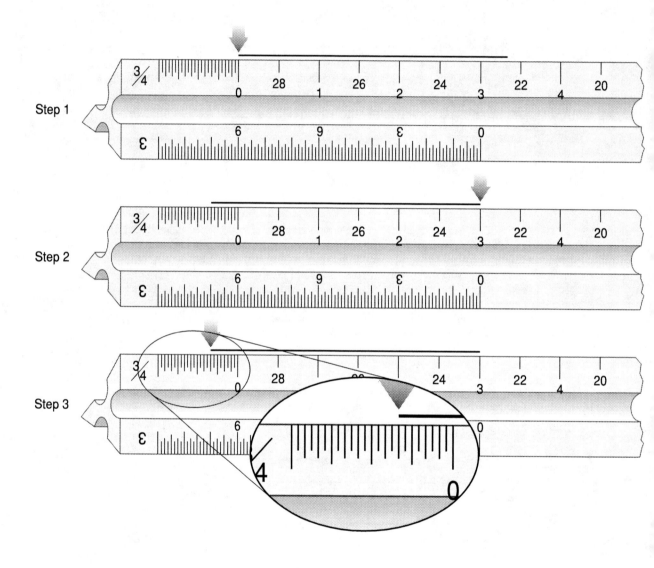

The Civil Engineer's Scale

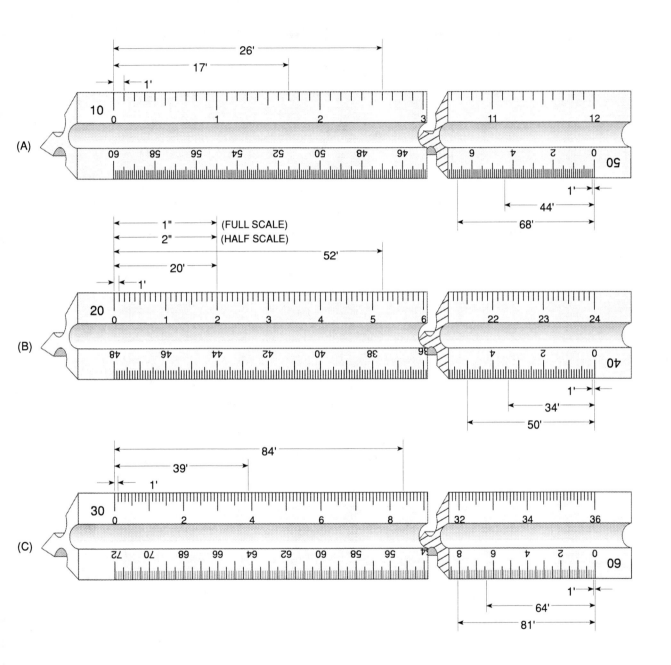

CIVIL ENGINEER'S SCALE

Divisions	Ratio	Scales Used with This Division			
10	1:1	1" = 1"	1" = 1"	1" = 10'	1" = 100'
20	1:2	1" = 2"		1" = 20'	1" = 200'
30	1:3	1" = 3"		1" = 30'	1" = 300'
40	1:4	1" = 4"		1" = 40'	1" = 400'
50	1:5	1" = 5"		1" = 50'	1" = 500'
60	1:6	1" = 6"		1" = 60'	1" = 600'

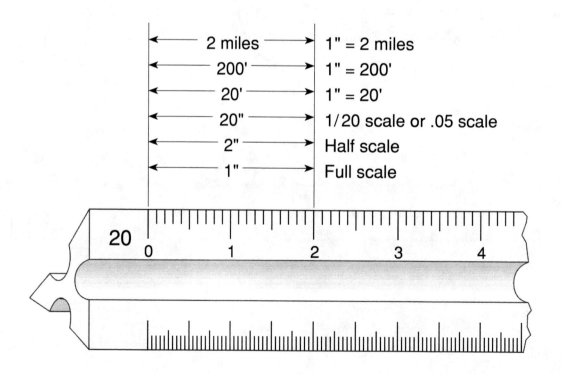

2 miles	1" = 2 miles
200'	1" = 200'
20'	1" = 20'
20"	1/20 scale or .05 scale
2"	Half scale
1"	Full scale

TM-43 Figure 3.61
Steps in Reading a Civil Engineer's Scale

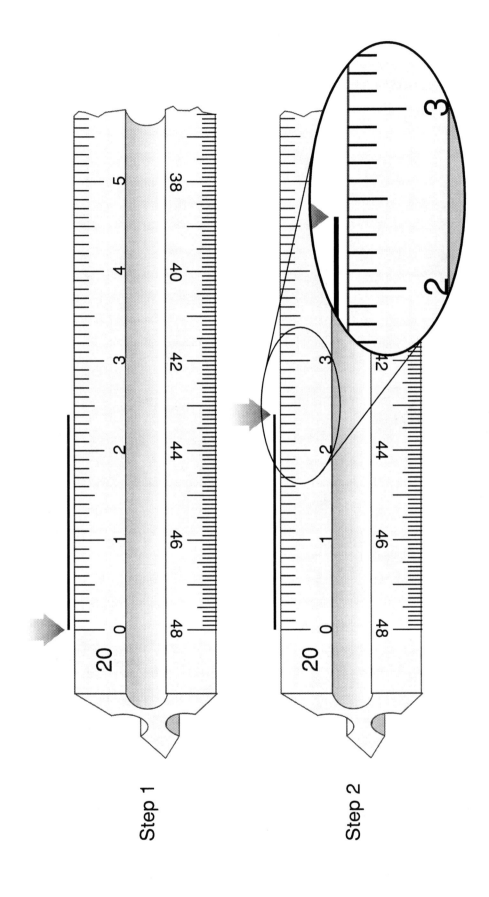

Step 1

Step 2

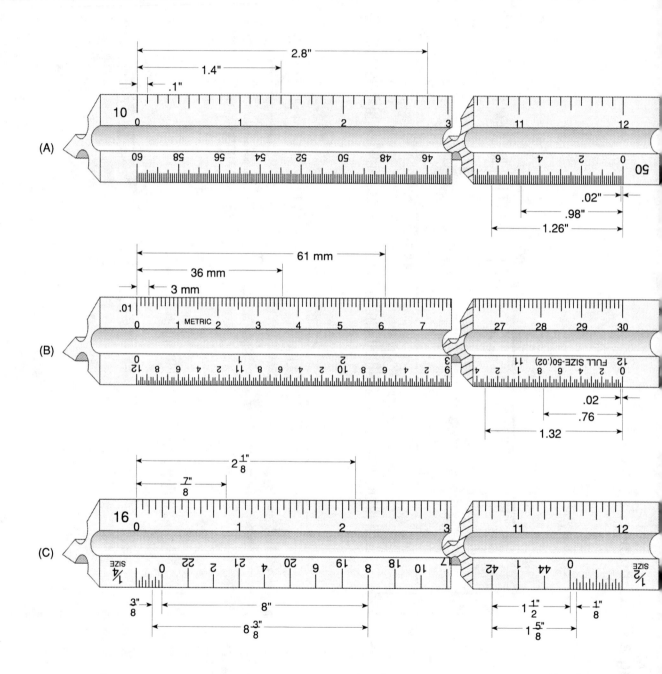

TM-45 Figure 3.63
Steps in Reading the Mechanical Engineer's Scale

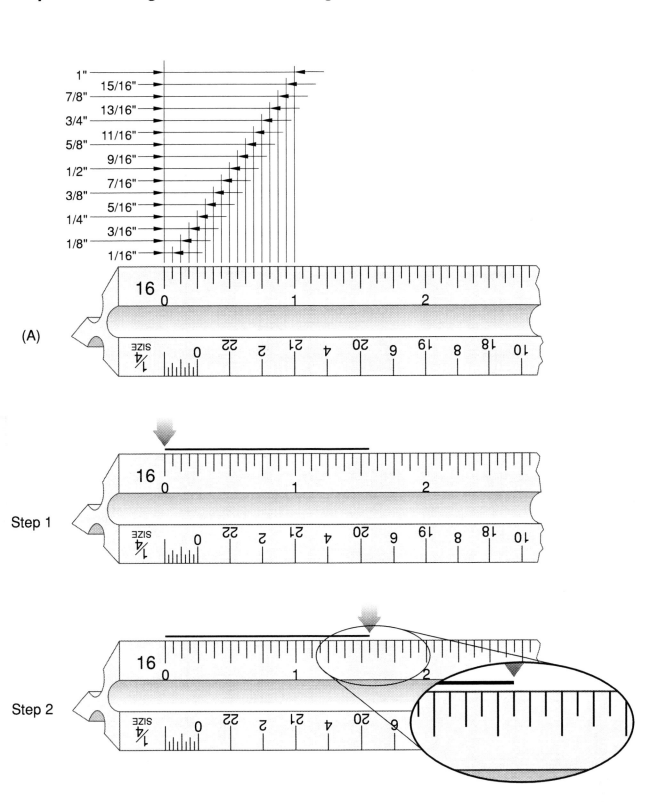

(A)

Step 1

Step 2

TM-46   Figure 3.64
Reading a 50 Scale

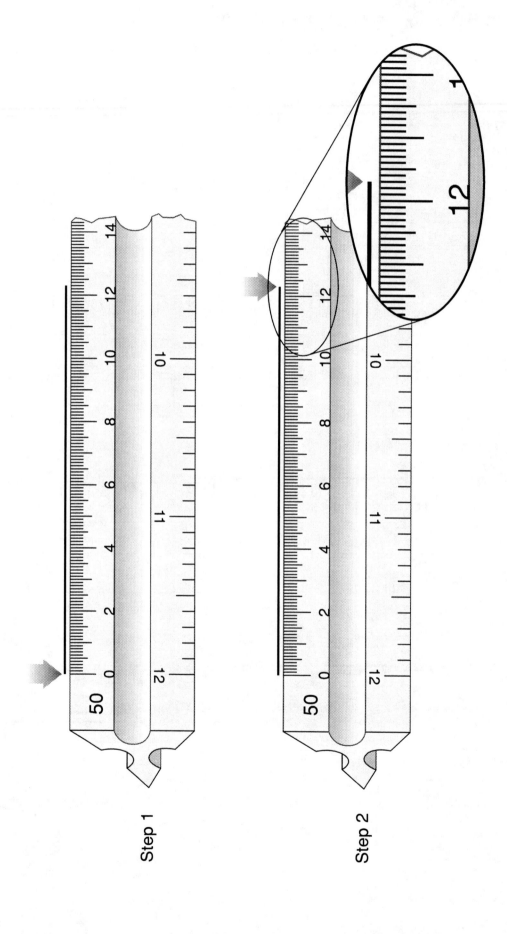

Step 1

Step 2

TM-47 Figure 3.65
Reading a Half-Size Scale

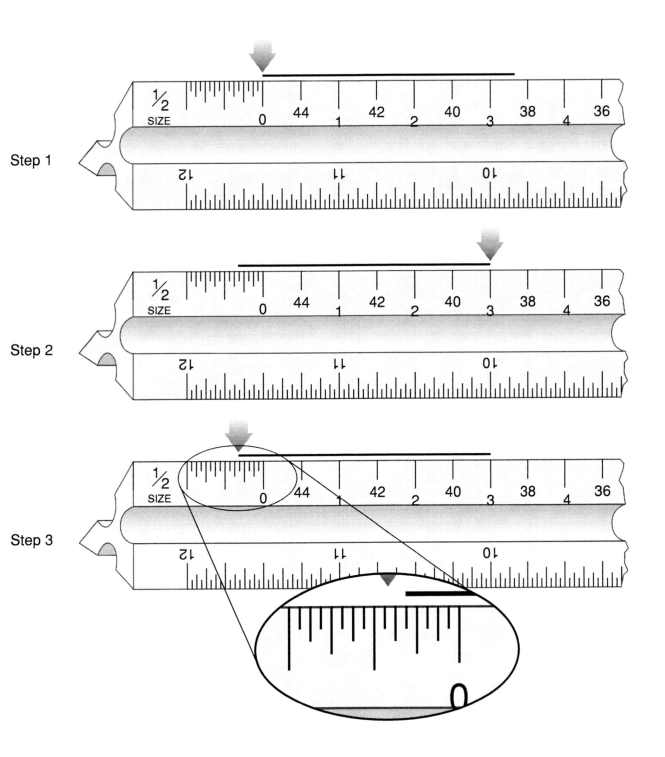

TM-48   Figure 3.66
The Metric Scale for Using SI Units

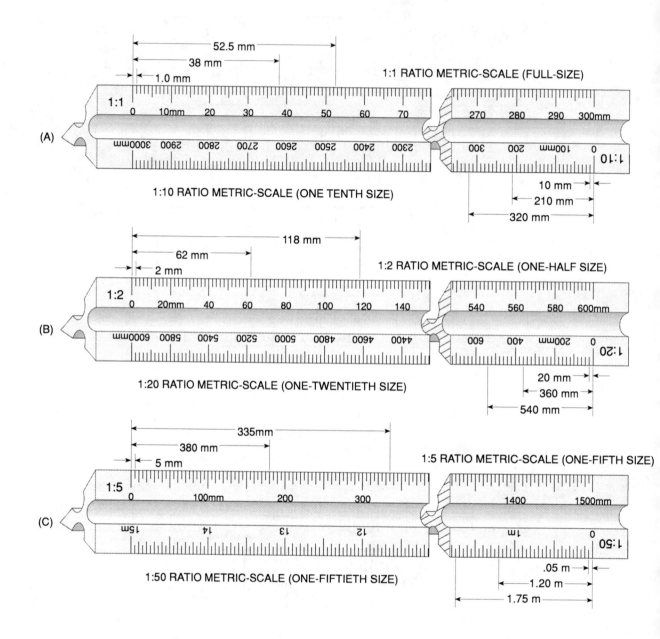

TM-49   Figure 3.67
Reading the Full and 1:20 Metric Scale

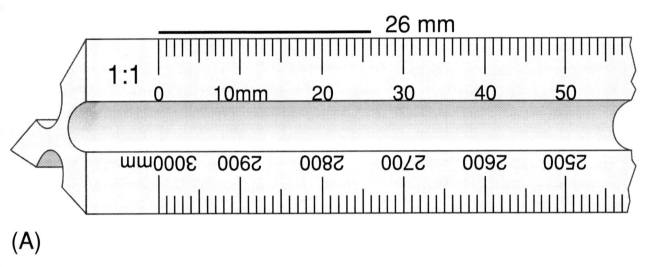

(A)

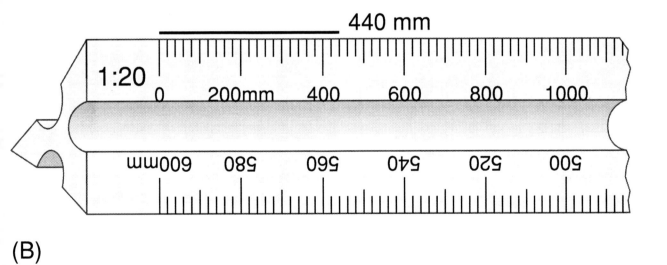

(B)

TM-50   Figure 3.77
**Examples of Good and Poor Drawing Techniques for Lines and Arcs,
Using Traditional Tools**

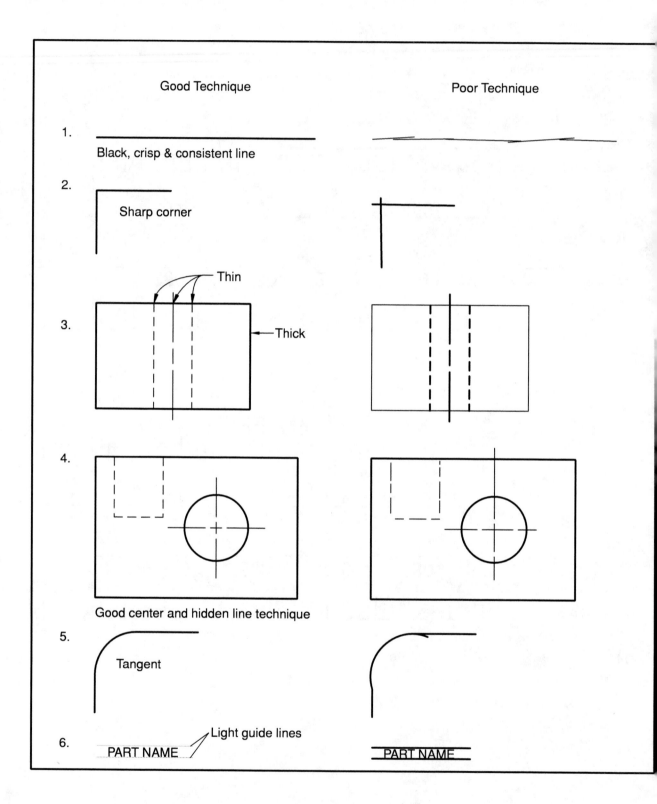

TM-51   Figure 4.9
Square (A), Isometric (B), and Perspective (C) Grids Used for Sketching

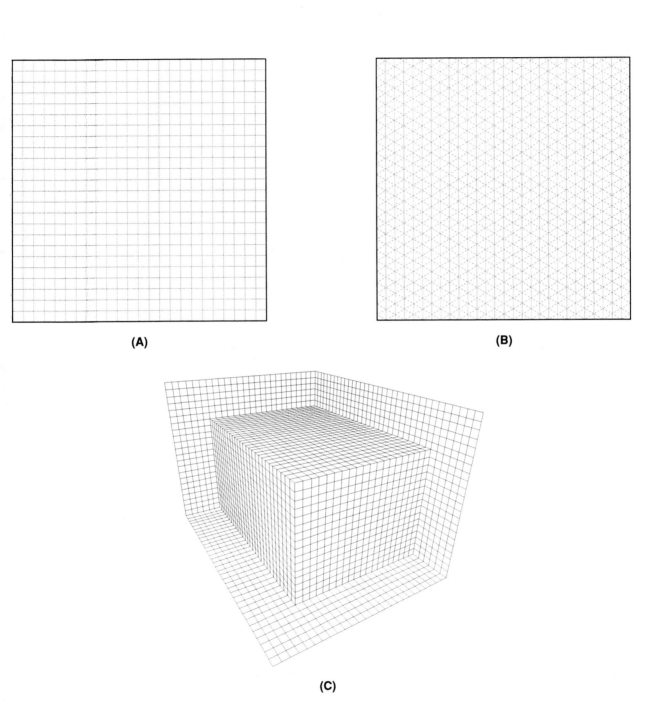

(A)

(B)

(C)

TM-52   Figure 4.11
Examples of Good and Bad Straight Line Technique

Yes

No!

No!

No!

TM-53   Figure 4.12
Sketching Lines

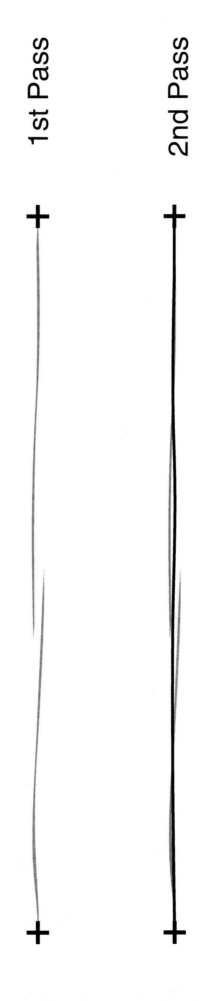

1st Pass

2nd Pass

**TM-54 Figure 4.14
Sketching a Circle**

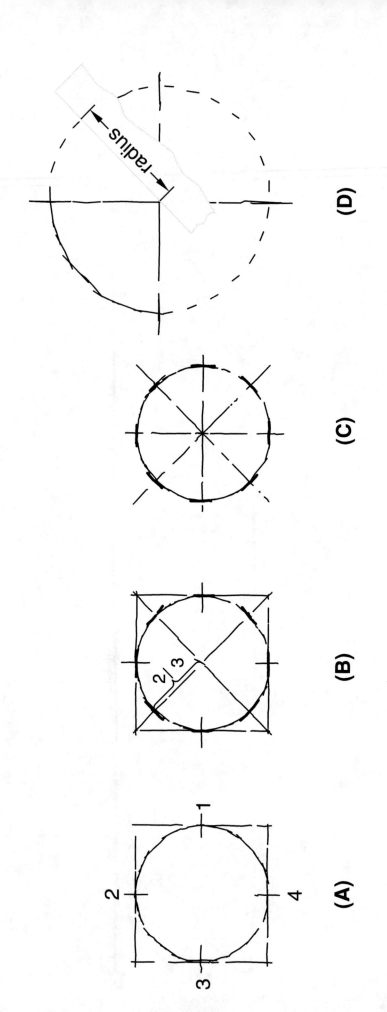

TM-55   Figure 4.16
Creating a Proportioned Sketch

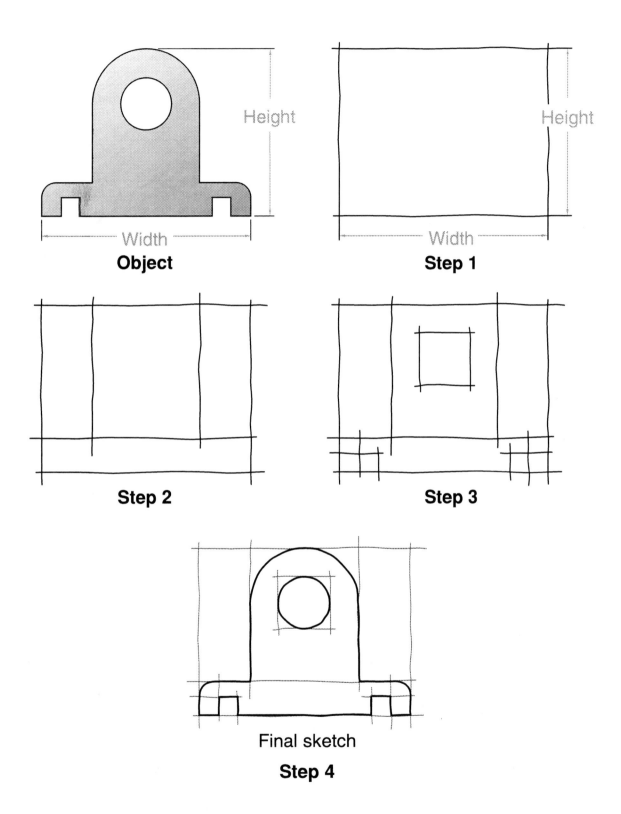

Object

Step 1

Step 2

Step 3

Final sketch

Step 4

TM-56   Figure 4.26
Classification of Sketches

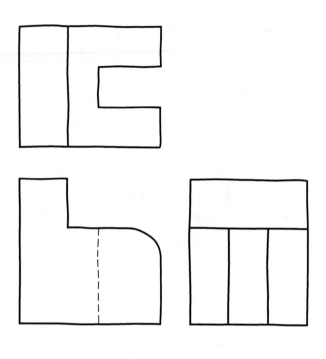

(A) Multiview

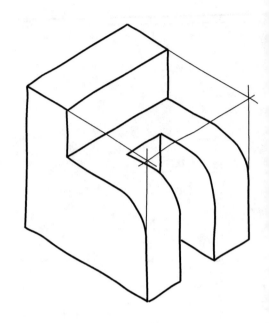

(B) Axonometric

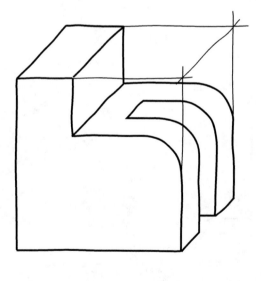

(C) Oblique

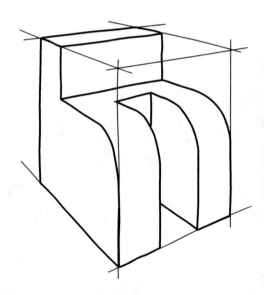

(D) Perspective

TM-57   Figure 4.29
The Basic Steps Used to Create an Isometric Sketch of an Object

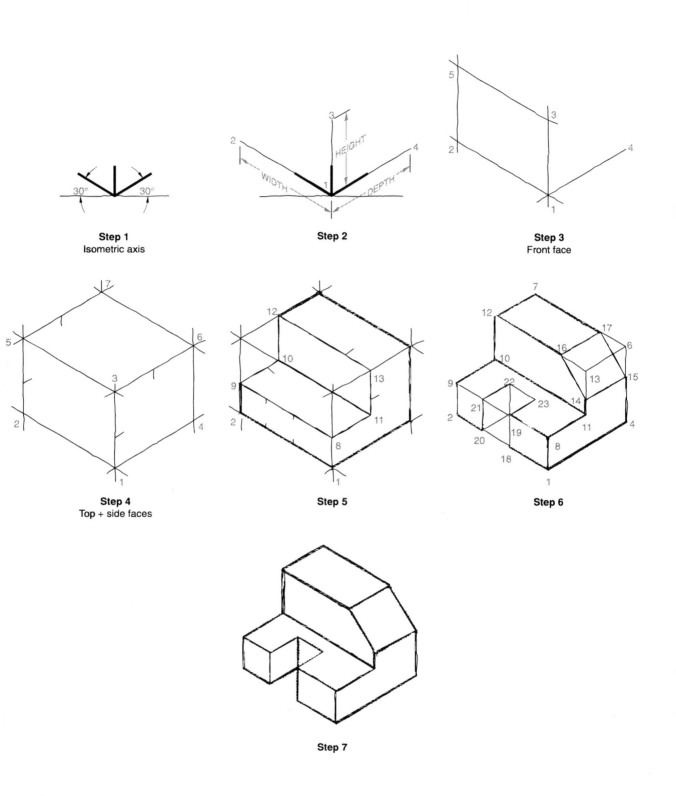

Step 1
Isometric axis

Step 2

Step 3
Front face

Step 4
Top + side faces

Step 5

Step 6

Step 7

TM-58 Figure 4.30
Isometric Representation of Circles

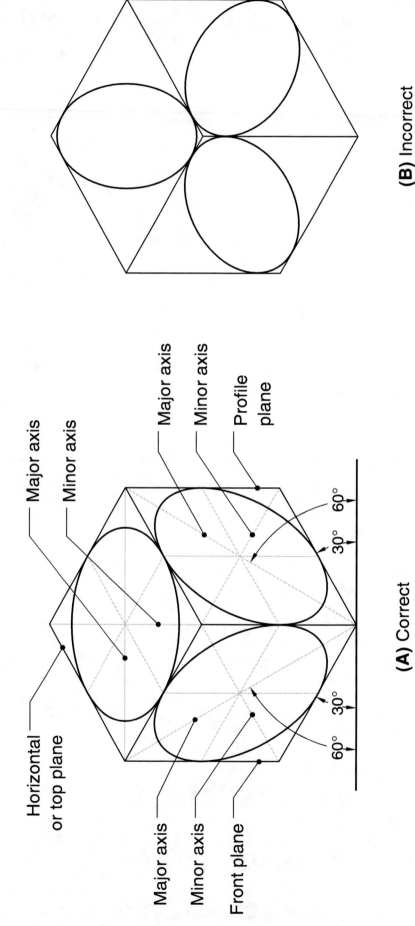

Major axis
Minor axis

Major axis
Minor axis
Profile plane

Horizontal or top plane

Major axis
Minor axis
Front plane

60° 60°
30°

30°
60°

(A) Correct

(B) Incorrect

TM-59   Figure 4.31
Sketching an Isometric Ellipse

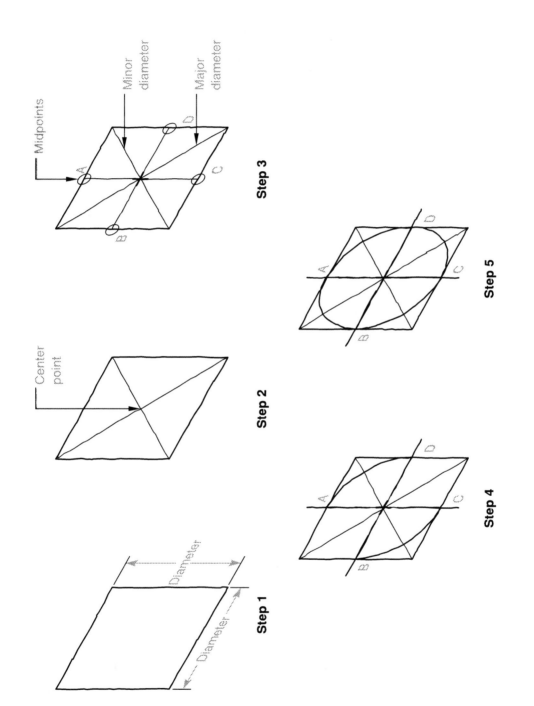

Step 1

Step 2

Step 3

Step 4

Step 5

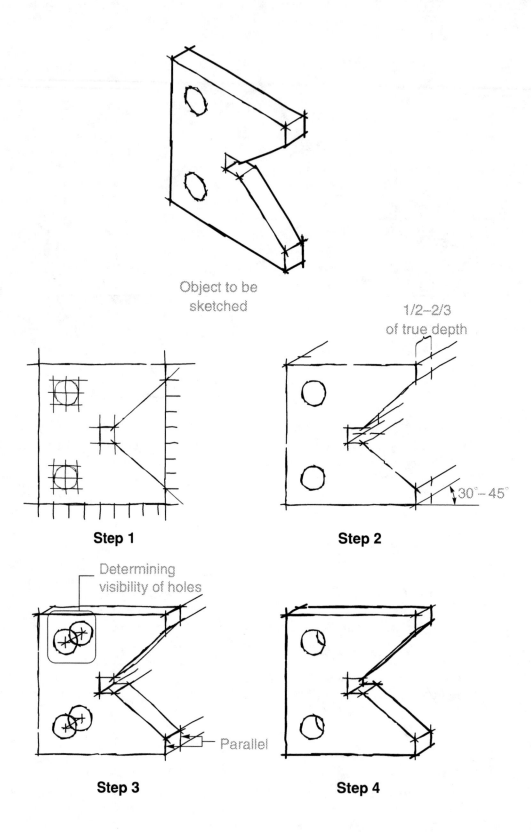

Object to be
sketched

1/2–2/3
of true depth

30°—45°

Step 1

Step 2

Determining
visibility of holes

Parallel

Step 3

Step 4

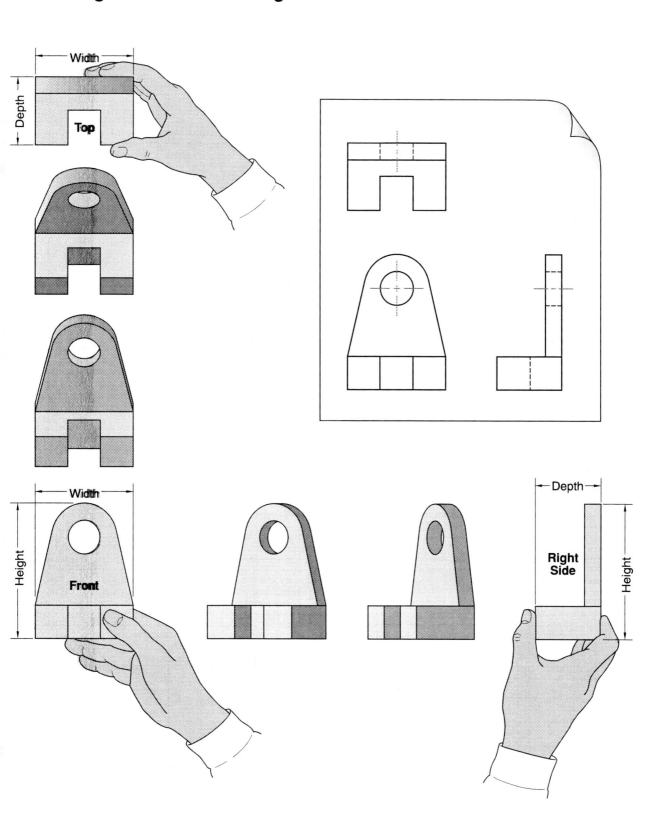

TM-62 Figure 4.41
Six Principal Views

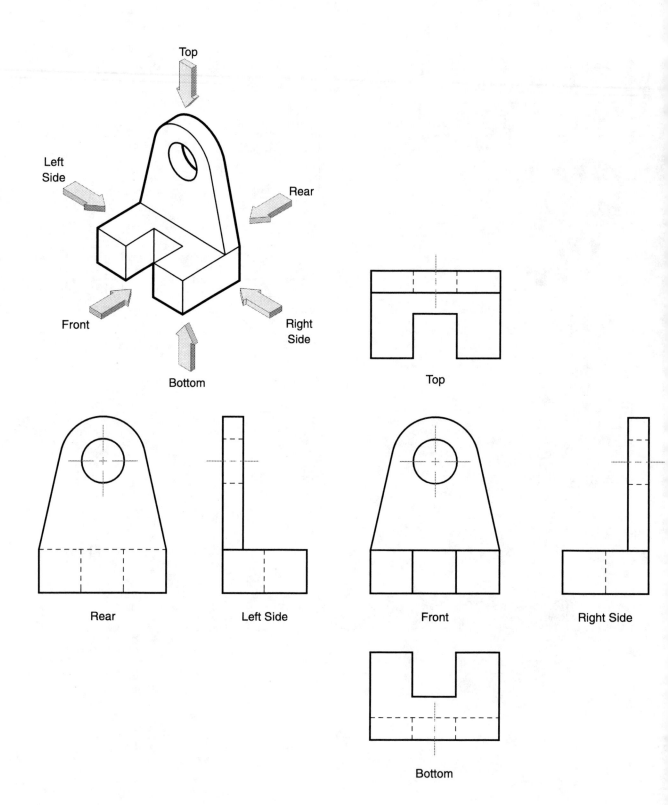

Top

Rear

Left Side

Front

Right Side

Bottom

Visible line　　　　　　　　　　.6mm

Hidden line　　　　　　　　　　.3mm

Center line　　　　　　　　　　.3mm

1.25

Dimension & Extension lines　　.3mm

Phantom line　　　　　　　　　.3mm

.6mm

Cutting plane lines　　　　　　　.6mm

Construction line　　　　　　　　.3mm

Section lines　　　　　　　　　　.3mm

TM-64 Figure 4.45
Drawing Conventions for Hidden Lines

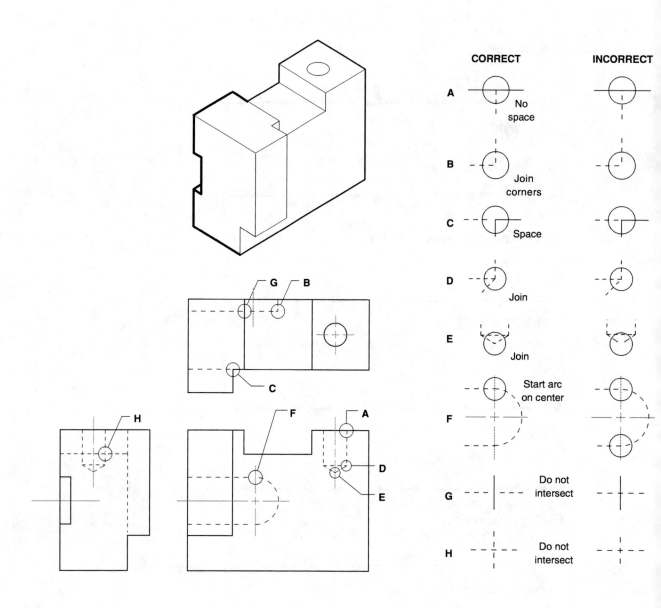

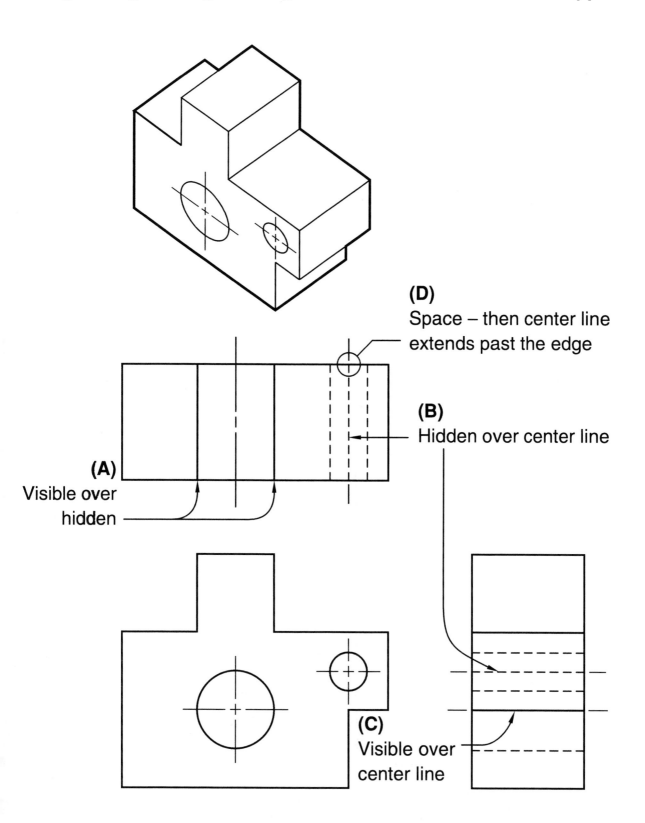

(D)
Space – then center line
extends past the edge

(B)
Hidden over center line

(A)
Visible over
hidden

(C)
Visible over
center line

TM-66   Figure 4.48
**An Engineering Drawing of a Cylinder, Showing the Application of
Center Lines**

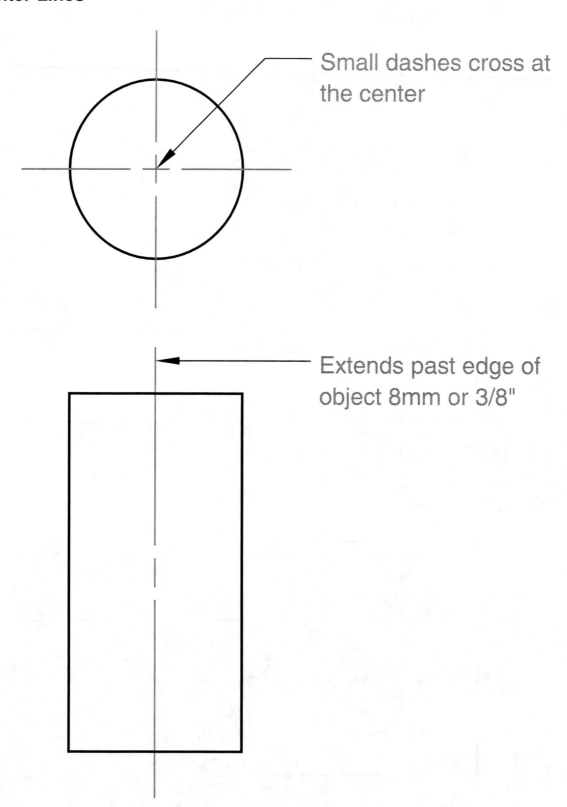

Small dashes cross at
the center

Extends past edge of
object 8mm or 3/8"

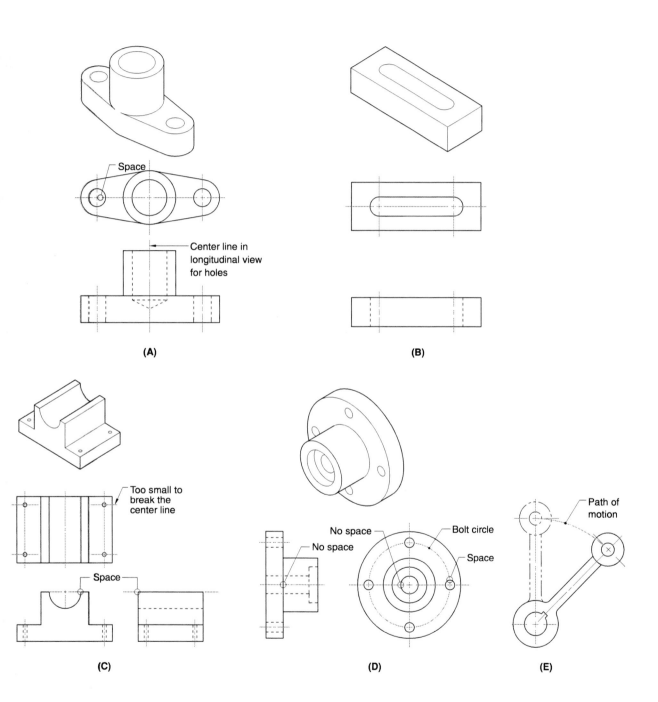

(A)

Space

Center line in
longitudinal view
for holes

(B)

(C)

Too small to
break the
center line

Space

(D)

No space

No space

Bolt circle

Space

(E)

Path of
motion

TM-68 Figure 4.53
Creating a Three-View Sketch

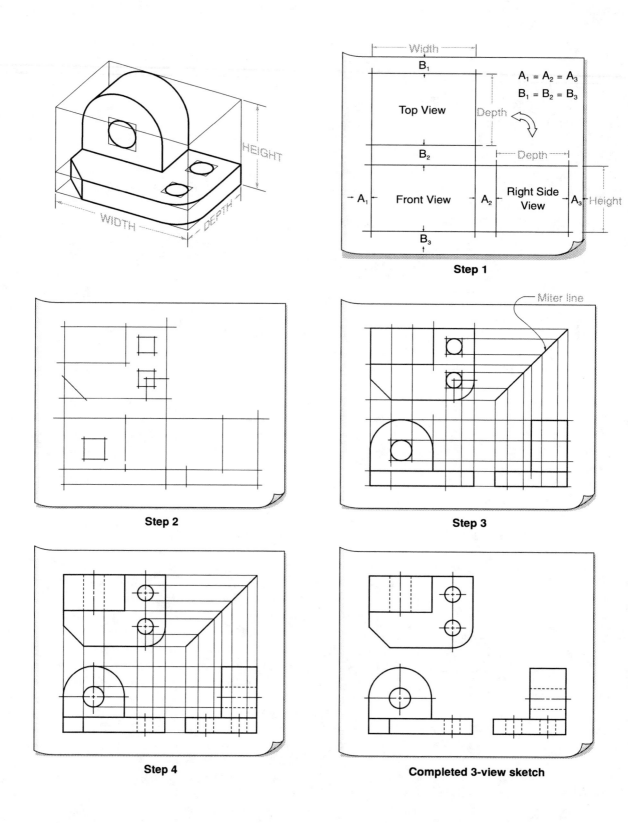

Step 1

Step 2

Step 3

Step 4

Completed 3-view sketch

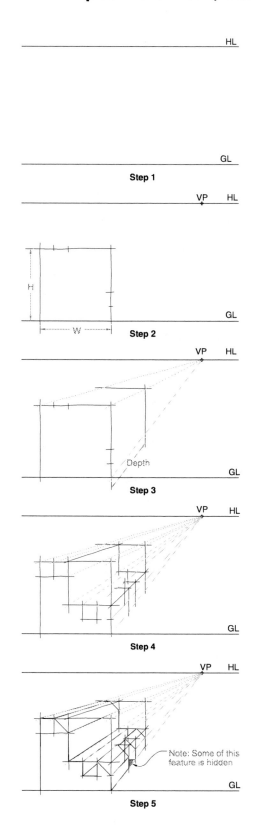

TM-70   Figure 4.71
Vertical Gothic Letter and Numeral Design, with Suggested Sequence of Strokes That Can Be Used as a Guide for Hand Lettering a Technical Drawing

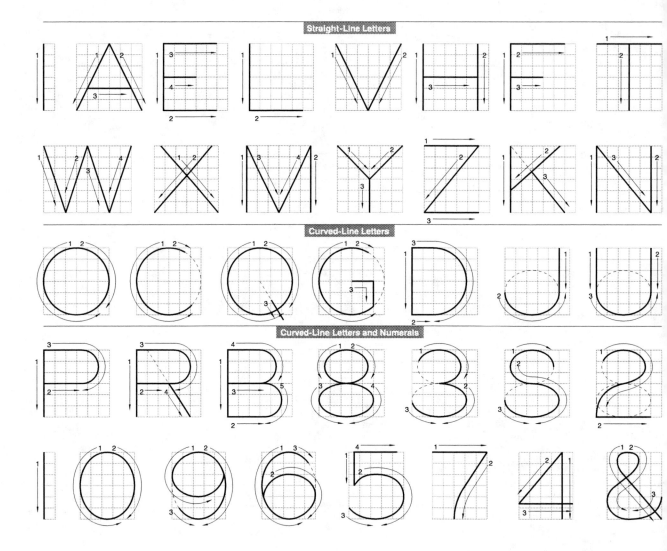

TM-71   Figure 4.72
Inclined Gothic Letter and Numeral Design, with Suggested Sequence of Strokes That Can Be Used as a Guide for Hand Lettering a Technical Drawing

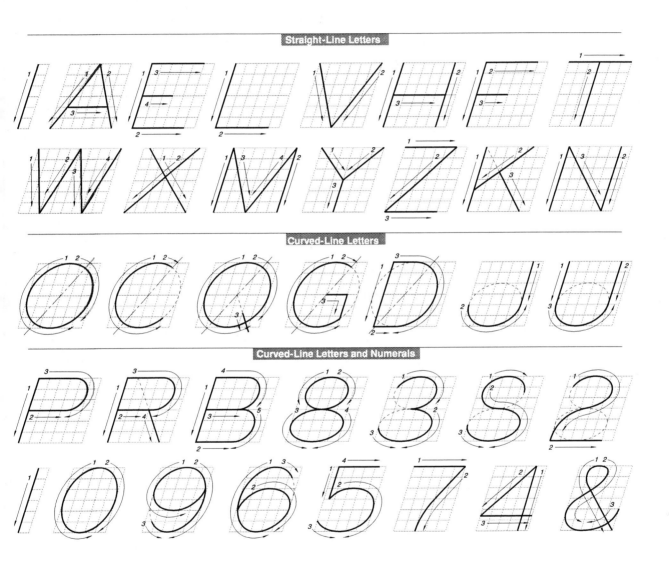

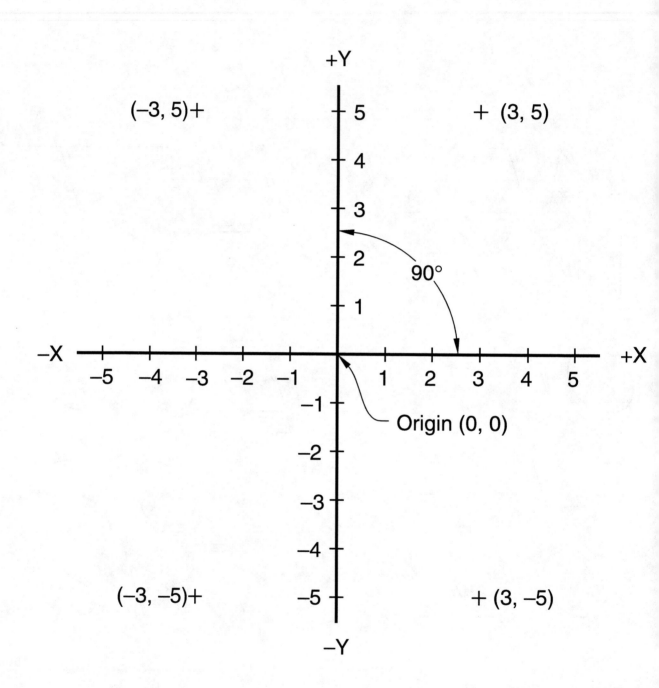

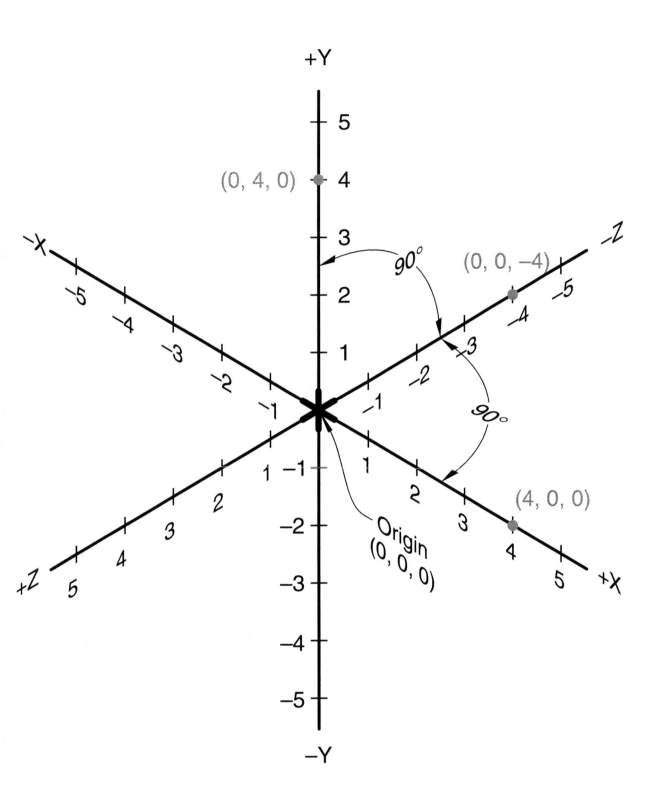

TM-74   Figure 6.8
Right-Hand Rule for Axes Directions

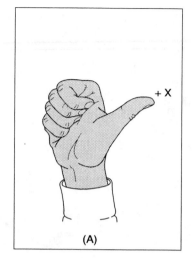

(A)

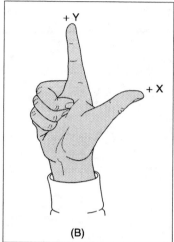

(B)

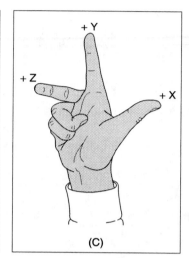

(C)

(D)

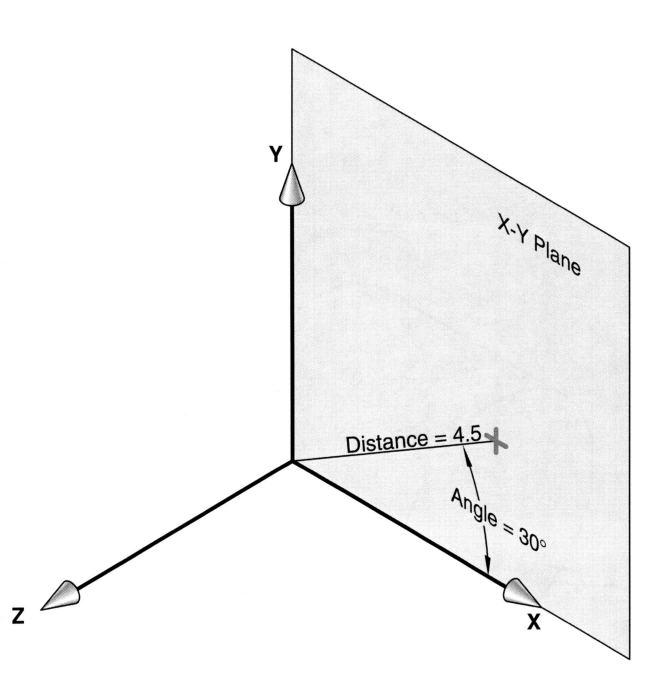

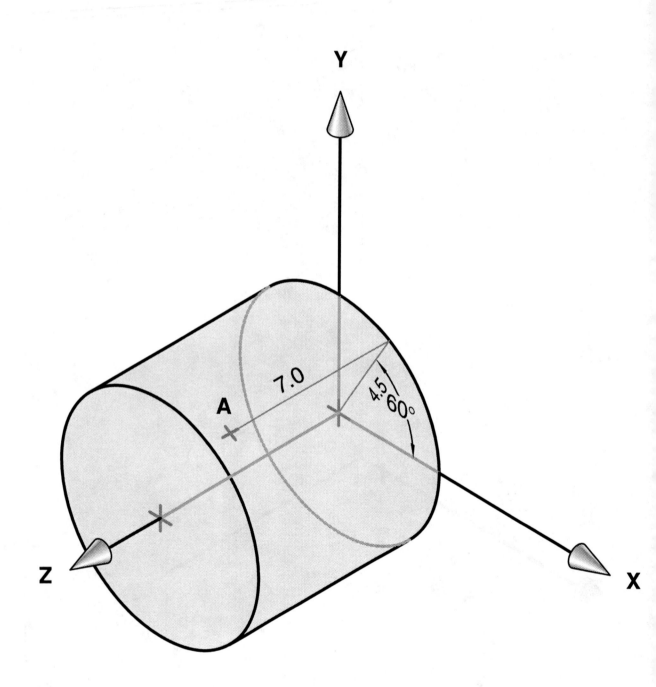

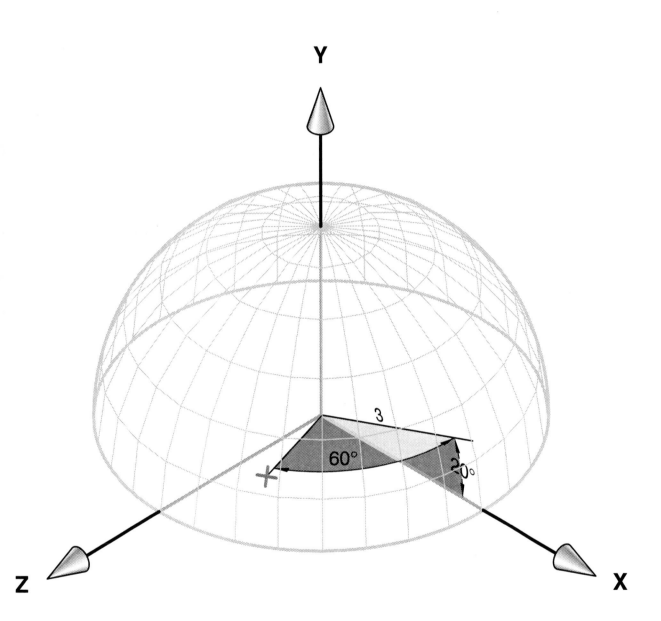

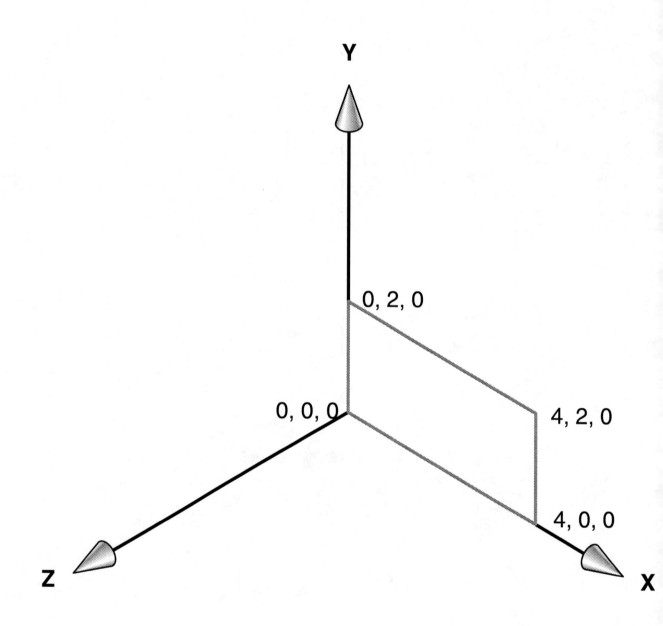

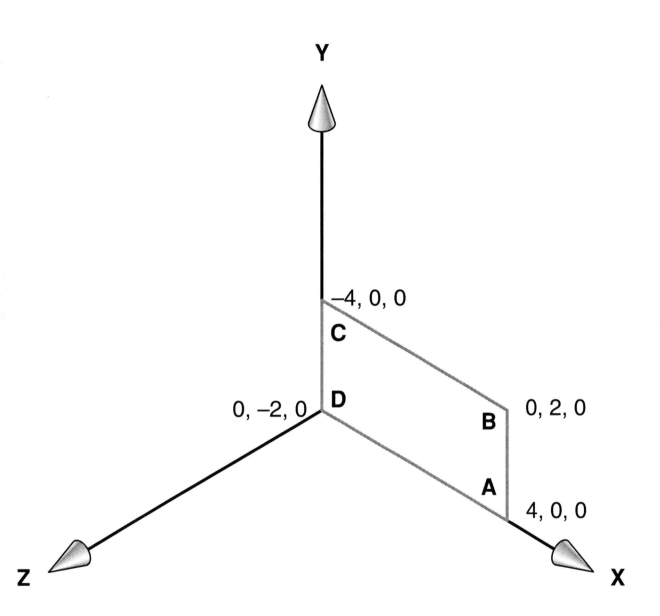

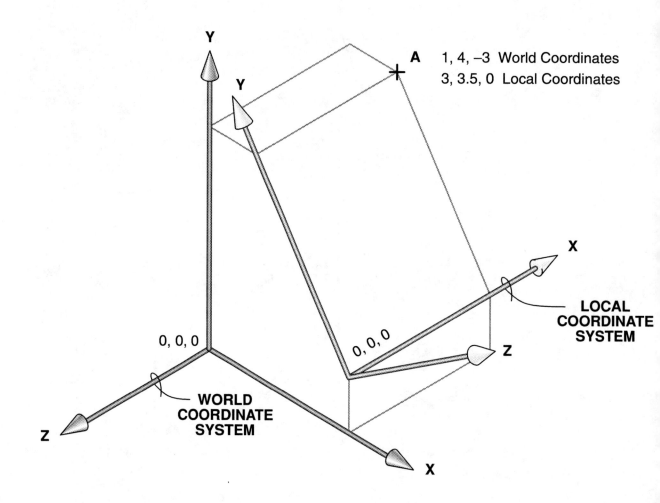

A   1, 4, −3 World Coordinates
3, 3.5, 0 Local Coordinates

LOCAL
COORDINATE
SYSTEM

0, 0, 0

0, 0, 0

WORLD
COORDINATE
SYSTEM

TM-81   Figure 6.15
Classification of Geometric Elements

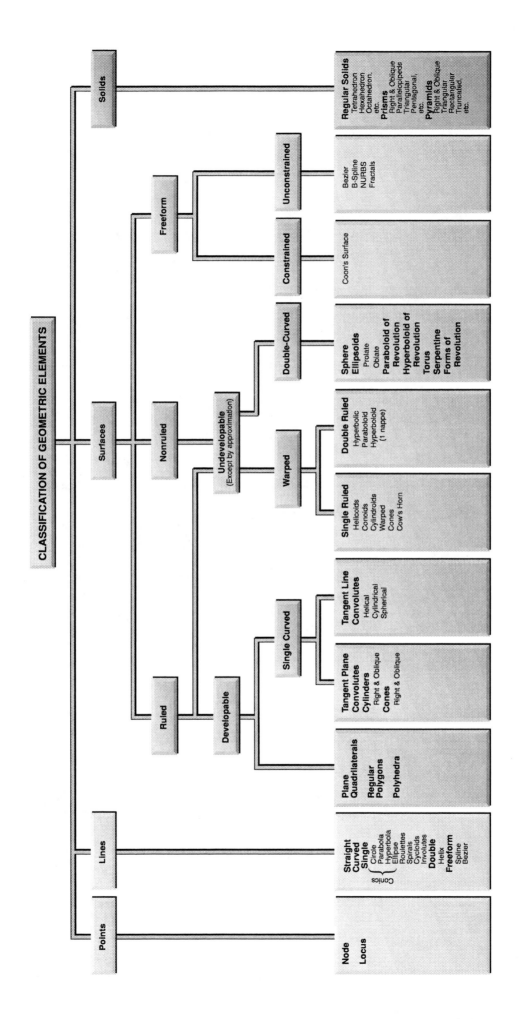

© The McGraw-Hill Companies, Inc., 1997

TM-82   Figure 6.16
Examples and Representation of Points

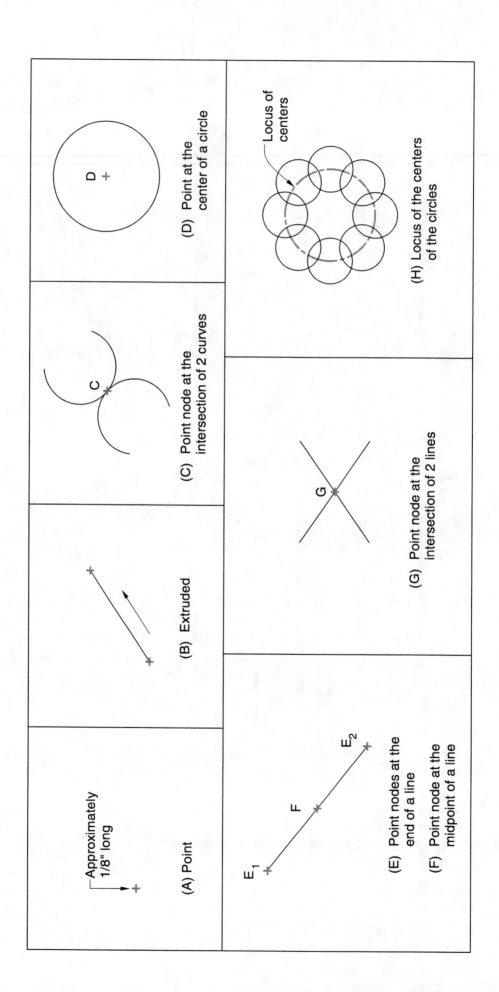

Parallel Line Condition

Intersecting Lines

Nonparallel Line Condition

Tangent Condition

Perpendicular Line Condition

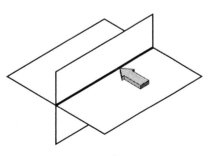

Line at Intersection of
Two Planes (Edge)

Tangent and Nontangent Conditions in 3-D Geometry

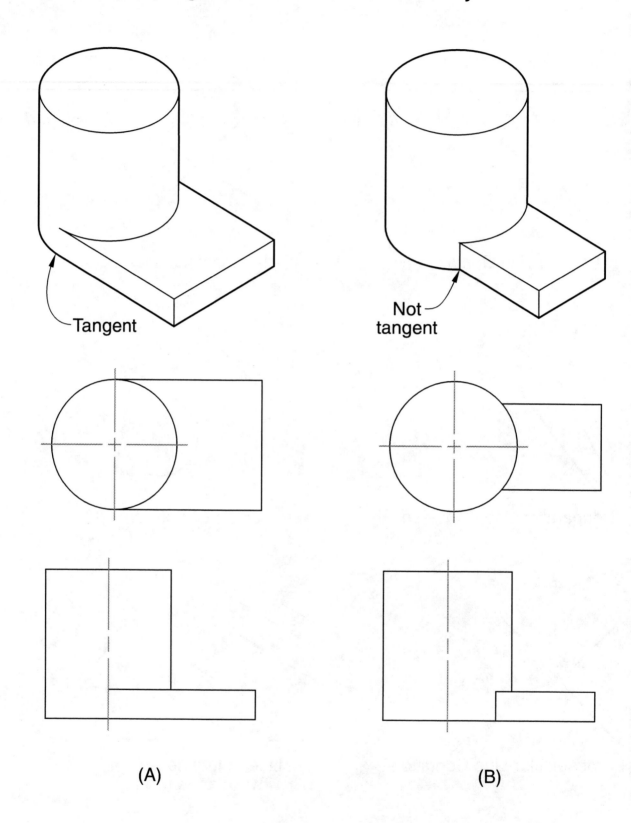

Tangent

Not tangent

(A)

(B)

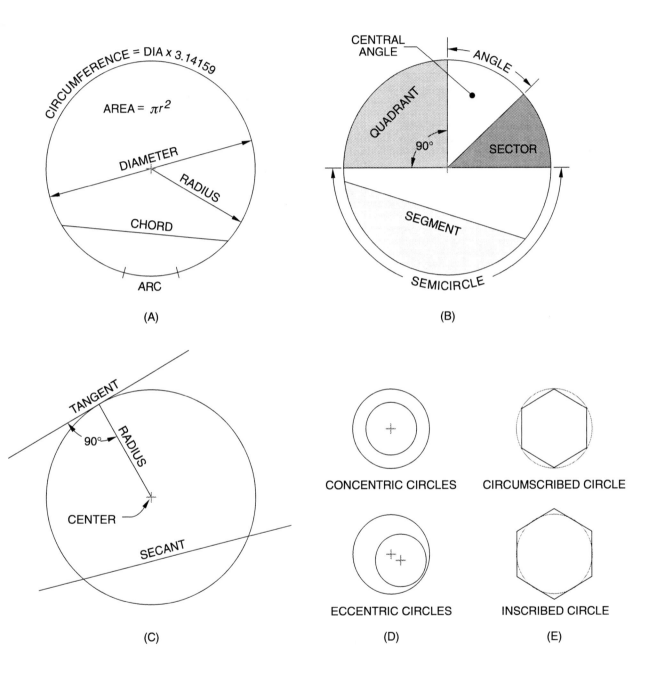

(A)

(B)

(C)

CONCENTRIC CIRCLES

CIRCUMSCRIBED CIRCLE

ECCENTRIC CIRCLES

INSCRIBED CIRCLE

(D)

(E)

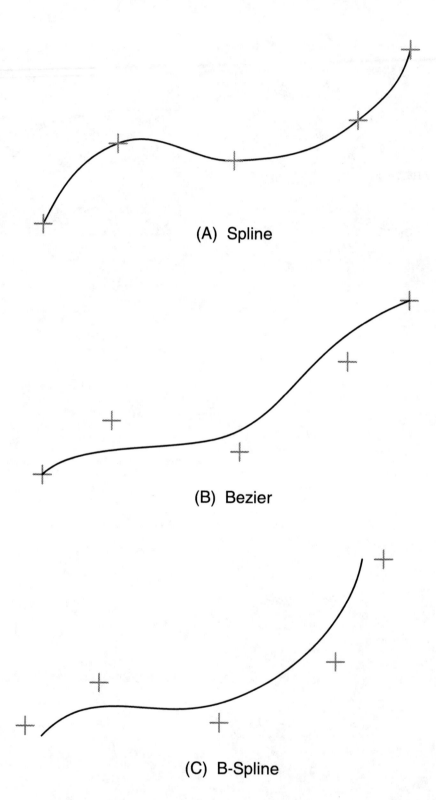

(A) Spline

(B) Bezier

(C) B-Spline

TM-87   Figure 6.93
Result of Changing Control Points

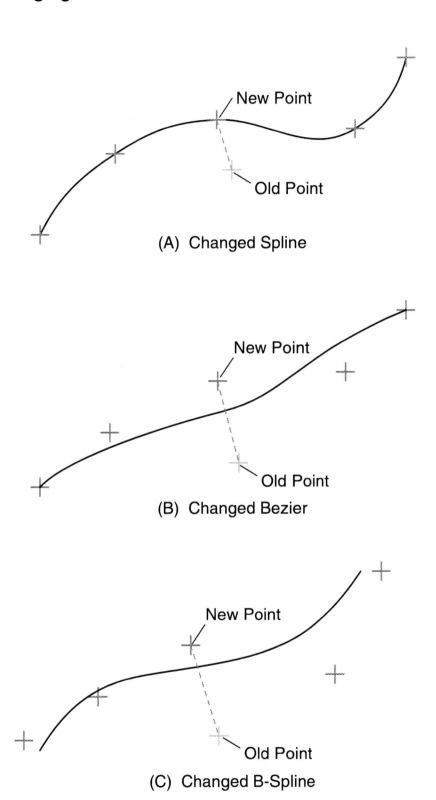

New Point

Old Point

(A)   Changed Spline

New Point

Old Point

(B)   Changed Bezier

New Point

Old Point

(C)   Changed B-Spline

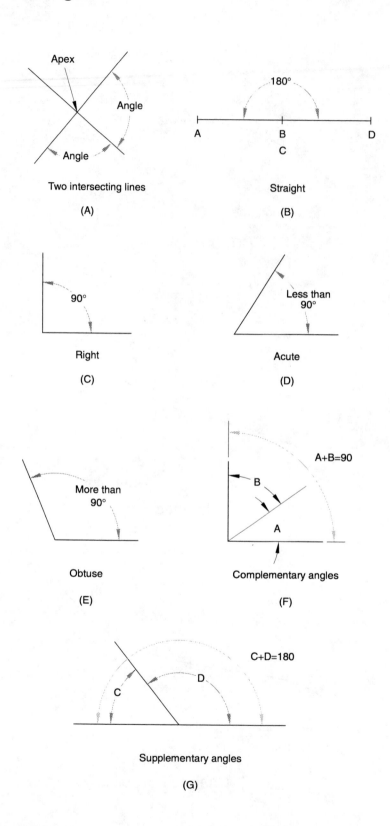

Apex

Angle

Angle

Two intersecting lines

(A)

180°

A   B   D

C

Straight

(B)

90°

Right

(C)

Less than
90°

Acute

(D)

More than
90°

Obtuse

(E)

A+B=90

B

A

Complementary angles

(F)

C+D=180

C   D

Supplementary angles

(G)

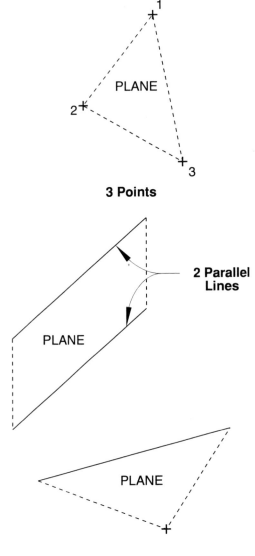

3 Points

2 Parallel
Lines

Line and a Point

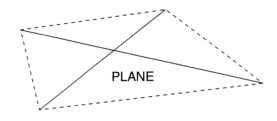

2 Intersecting Lines

TM-90 Figure 6.99
Examples of Surfaces Commonly Used in Engineering Design

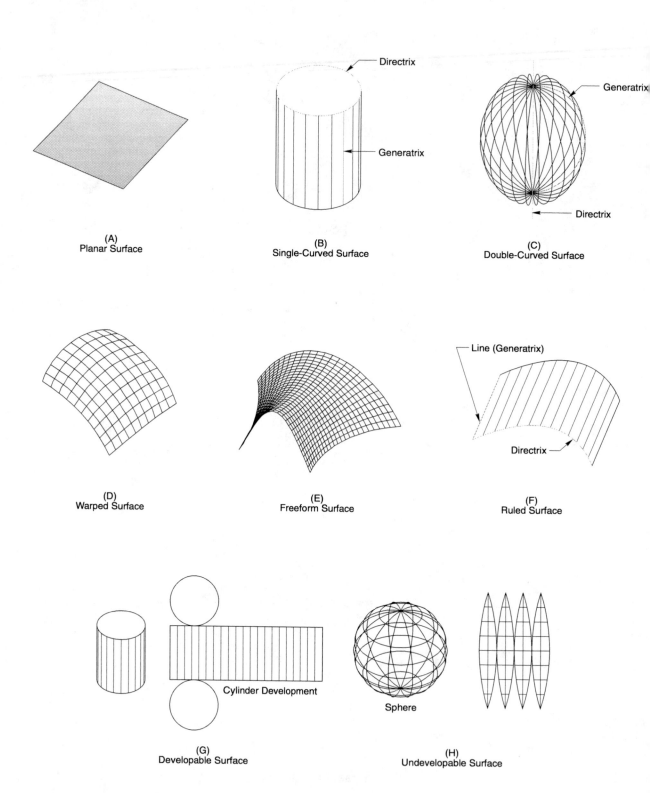

(A)
Planar Surface

(B)
Single-Curved Surface

(C)
Double-Curved Surface

(D)
Warped Surface

(E)
Freeform Surface

(F)
Ruled Surface

Cylinder Development

Sphere

(G)
Developable Surface

(H)
Undevelopable Surface

Example of a Wireframe Model Lacking Uniqueness

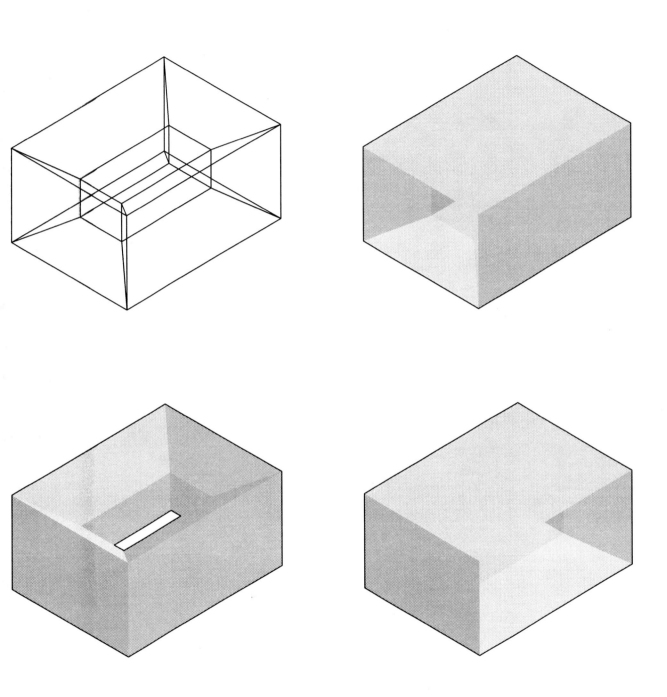

TM-92   Figure 7.20
The Three Boolean Operations: Union, Difference, and Intersection

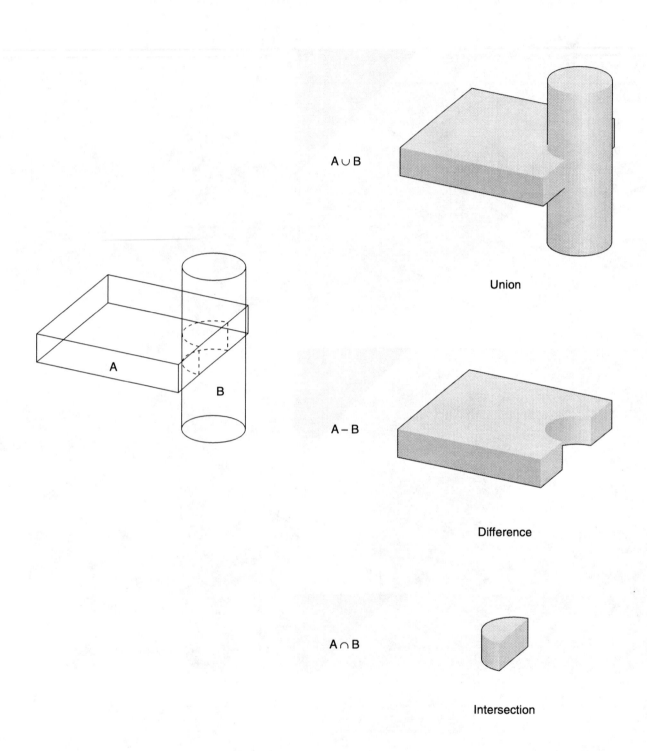

A ∪ B

Union

A − B

Difference

A ∩ B

Intersection

TM-93   Figure 7.21
The Effects of Ordering of Operands in a Difference Operation

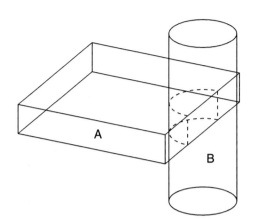

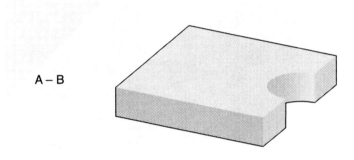

A – B

B – A

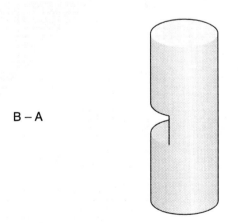

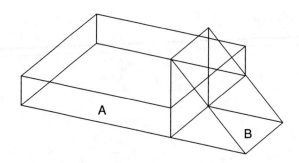

A   B

A ∪ B

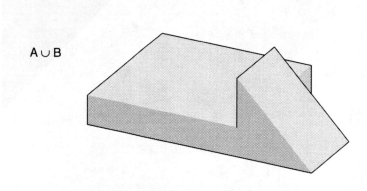

A − B

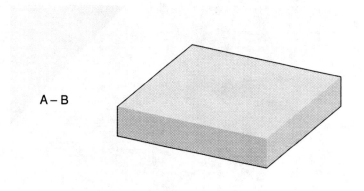

A ∩ B   Ø
                   Null object

A Camera Described Using CSG Modeling

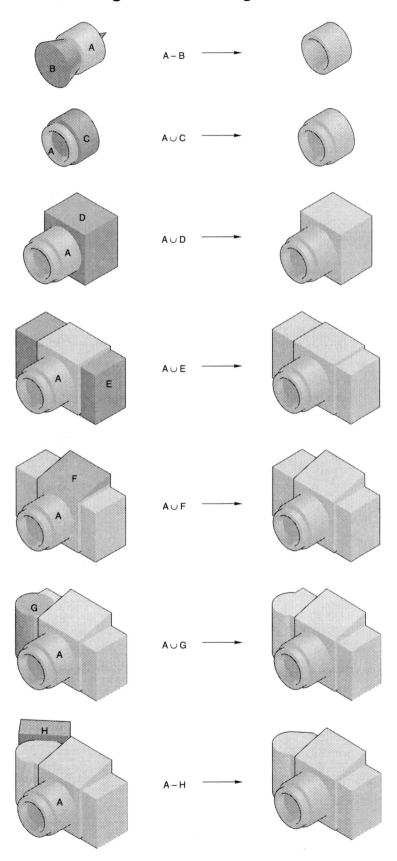

TM-96 Figure 7.25
Examples of Local Coordinate Systems

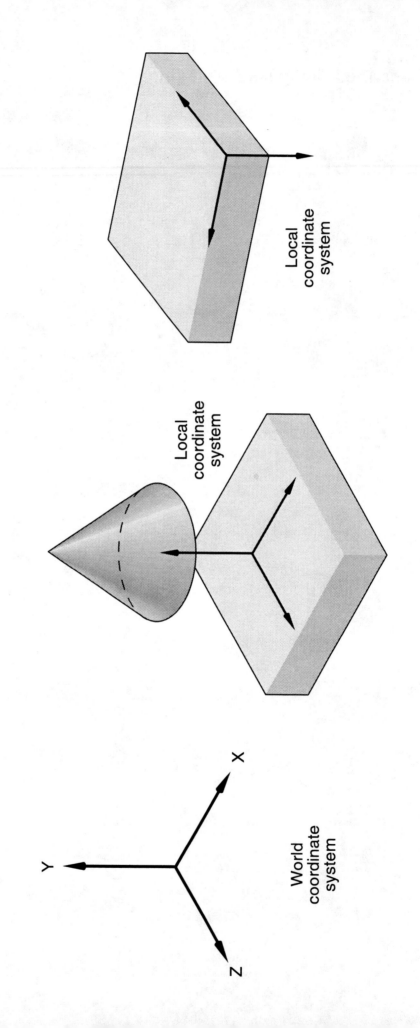

TM-97   Figure 7.26
Constructing a Wireframe Model

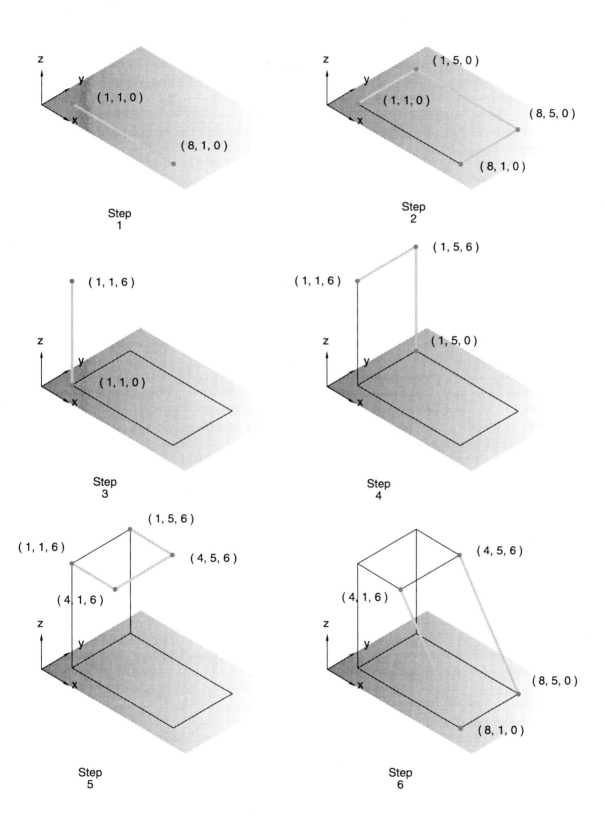

TM-98   Figure 7.29
Types of Linear Sweeping Operations

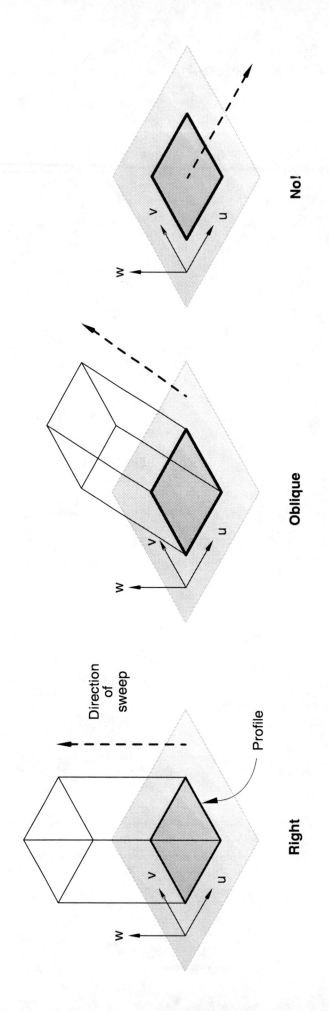

Direction of sweep

Profile

Right

Oblique

No!

TM-99   Figure 7.31
Examples of Circular Sweeping Operations

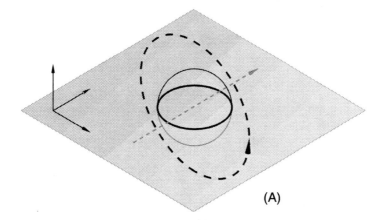

(A)

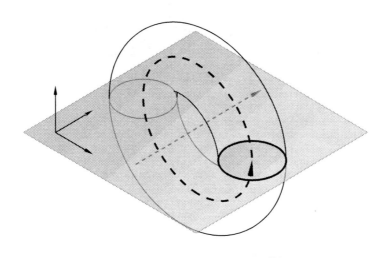

(B)

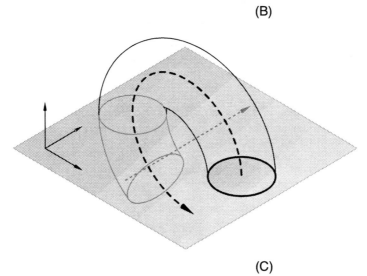

(C)

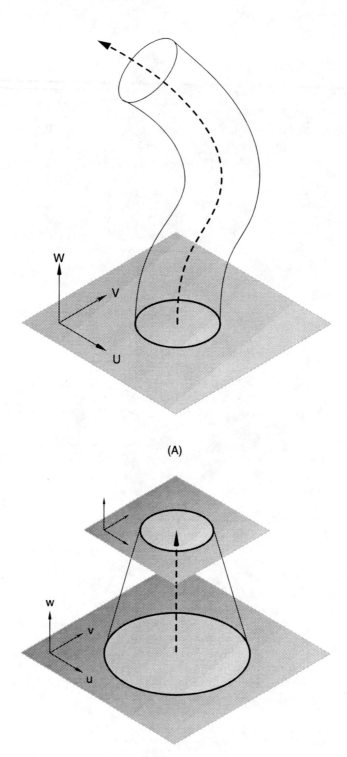

(A)

(B)

Scaling

Reflection

Rotate

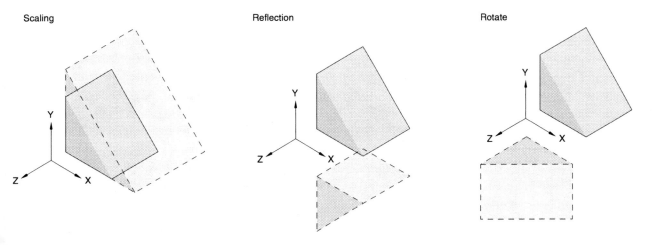

Translate

Shearing

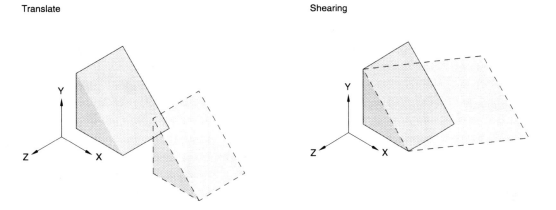

TM-102 Figure 7.50
Model Building Using Tool Solids

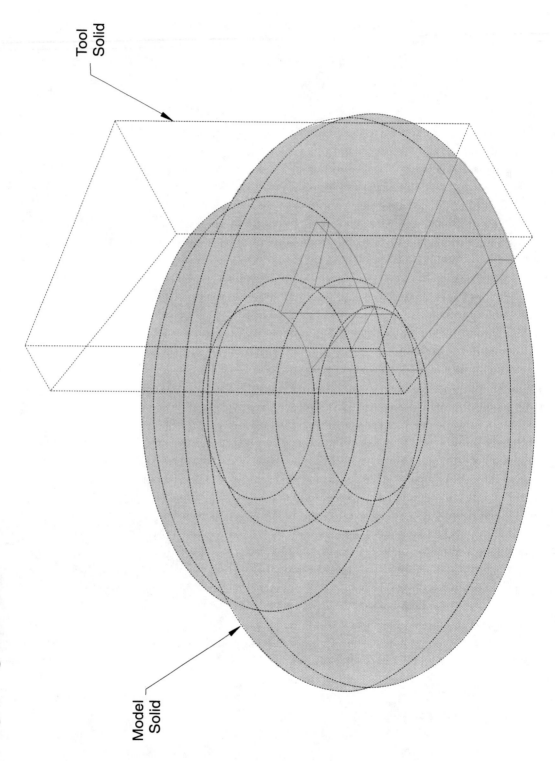

Tool
Solid

Model
Solid

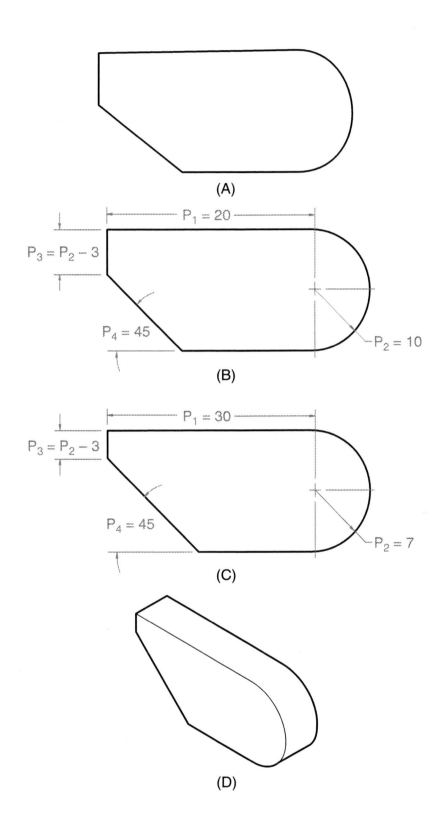

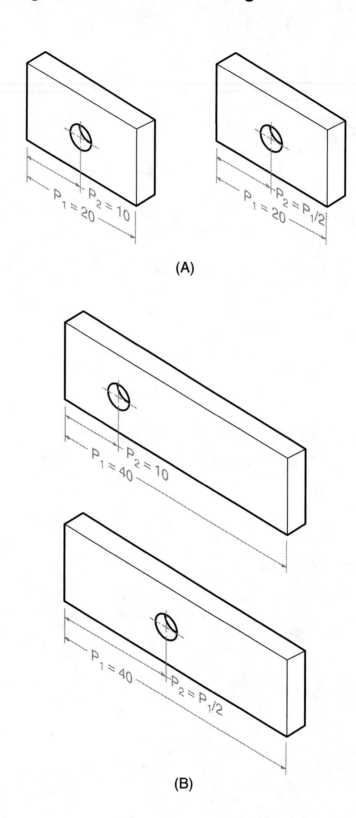

TM-104 Figure 7.53
The Effect of Design Intent on Model Changes

(A)

(B)

TM-105 Figure 8.1
Projection Methods

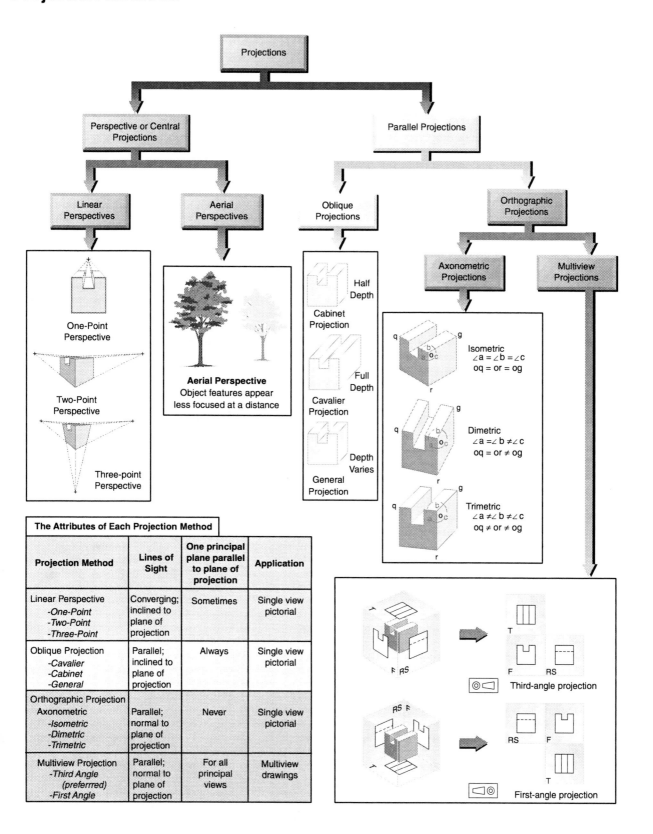

Projections

Perspective or Central Projections

Parallel Projections

Linear Perspectives

One-Point Perspective

Two-Point Perspective

Three-point Perspective

Aerial Perspectives

Aerial Perspective
Object features appear less focused at a distance

Oblique Projections

Half Depth
Cabinet Projection

Full Depth
Cavalier Projection

Depth Varies
General Projection

Orthographic Projections

Axonometric Projections

Isometric
$\angle a = \angle b = \angle c$
oq = or = og

Dimetric
$\angle a = \angle b \neq \angle c$
oq = or $\neq$ og

Trimetric
$\angle a \neq \angle b \neq \angle c$
oq $\neq$ or $\neq$ og

Multiview Projections

Third-angle projection

First-angle projection

The Attributes of Each Projection Method

Projection Method	Lines of Sight	One principal plane parallel to plane of projection	Application
Linear Perspective -One-Point -Two-Point -Three-Point	Converging; inclined to plane of projection	Sometimes	Single view pictorial
Oblique Projection -Cavalier -Cabinet -General	Parallel; inclined to plane of projection	Always	Single view pictorial
Orthographic Projection Axonometric -Isometric -Dimetric -Trimetric	Parallel; normal to plane of projection	Never	Single view pictorial
Multiview Projection -Third Angle (preferrred) -First Angle	Parallel; normal to plane of projection	For all principal views	Multiview drawings

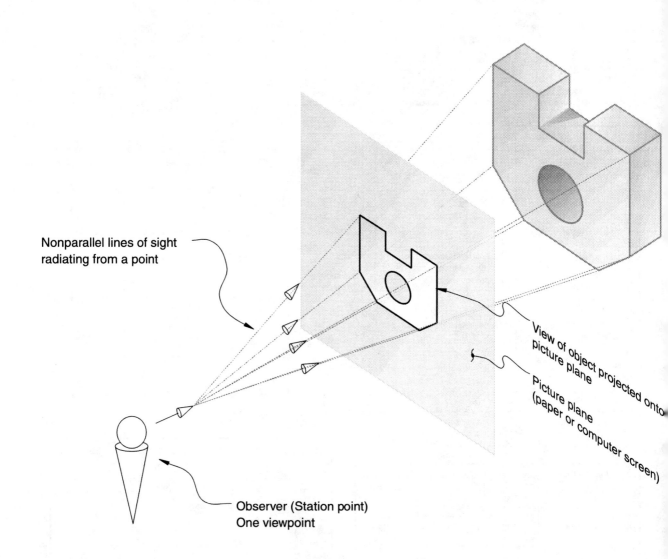

Nonparallel lines of sight
radiating from a point

View of object projected onto
picture plane

Picture plane
(paper or computer screen)

Observer (Station point)
One viewpoint

TM-107   Figure 8.5
Parallel Projection

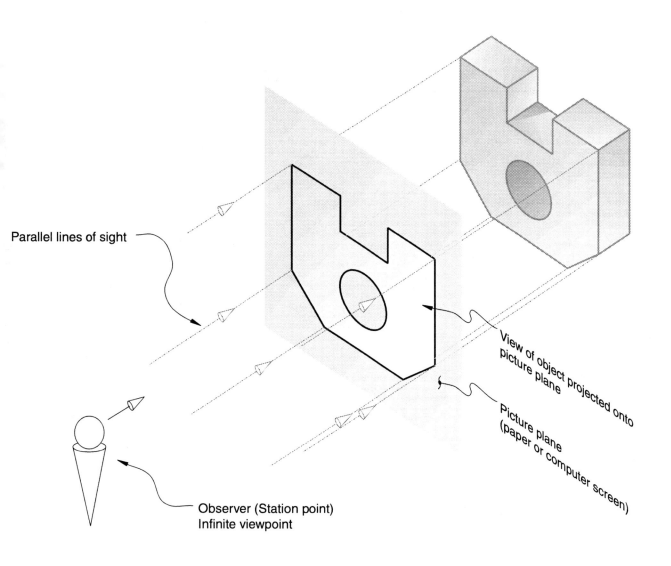

Parallel lines of sight

View of object projected onto
picture plane

Picture plane
(paper or computer screen)

Observer (Station point)
Infinite viewpoint

TM-108   Figure 8.7
Orthographic Projection

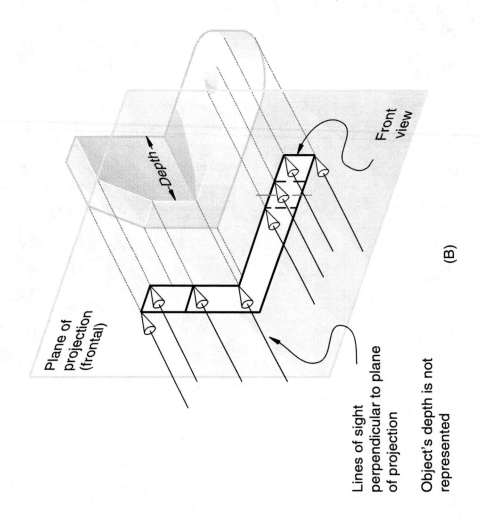

Plane of
projection
(frontal)

Depth

Front
view

Lines of sight
perpendicular to plane
of projection

Object's depth is not
represented

(B)

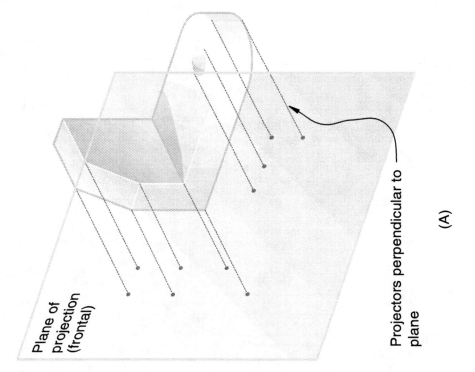

Plane of projection
(frontal)

Projectors perpendicular to
plane

(A)

TM-109   Figure 8.17
Object Suspended in a Glass Box, Producing the Six Principal Views

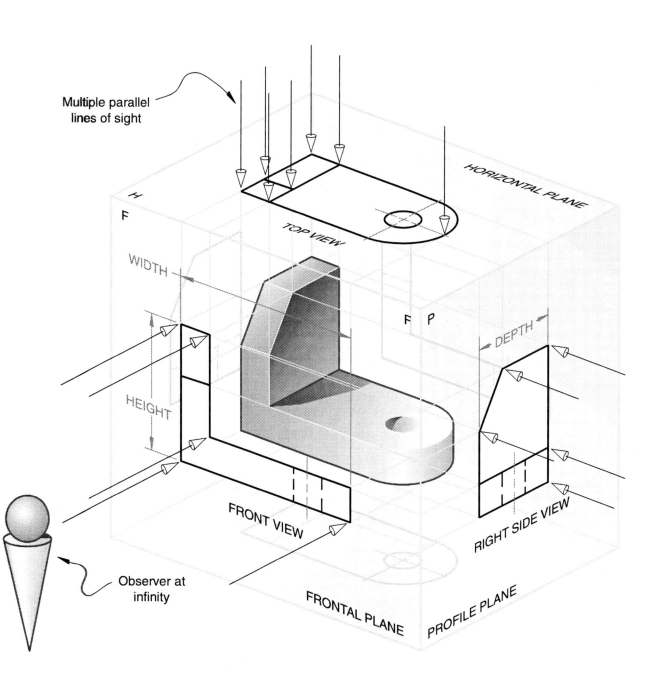

Multiple parallel lines of sight

HORIZONTAL PLANE

H

F

TOP VIEW

WIDTH

F P

DEPTH

HEIGHT

FRONT VIEW

RIGHT SIDE VIEW

Observer at infinity

FRONTAL PLANE

PROFILE PLANE

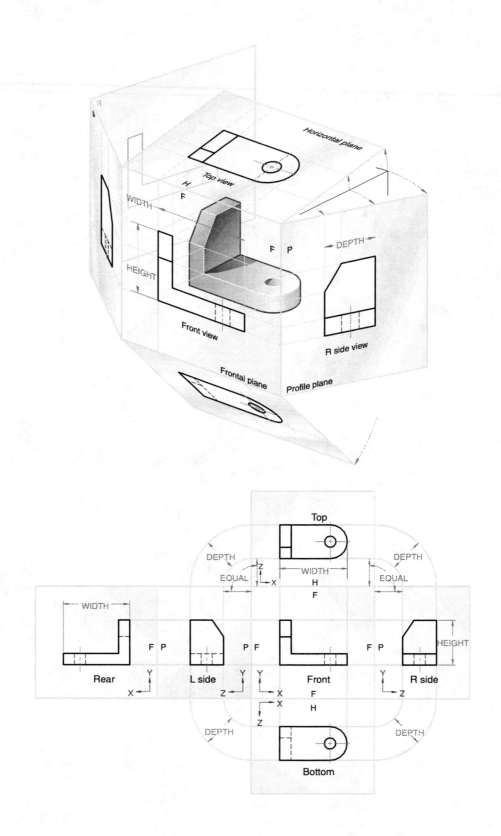

Projection line

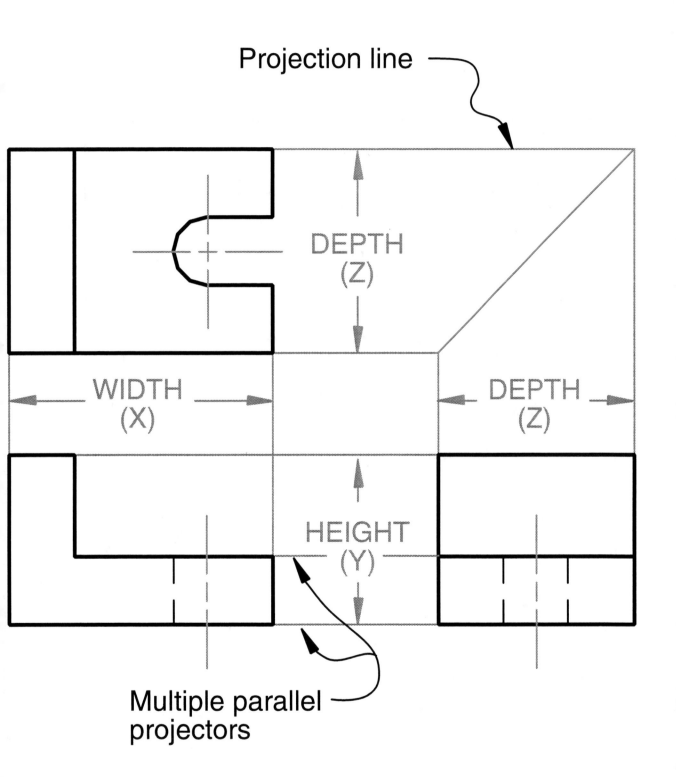

DEPTH
(Z)

WIDTH
(X)

DEPTH
(Z)

HEIGHT
(Y)

Multiple parallel
projectors

TM-112   Figure 8.21
Alternate View Arrangement

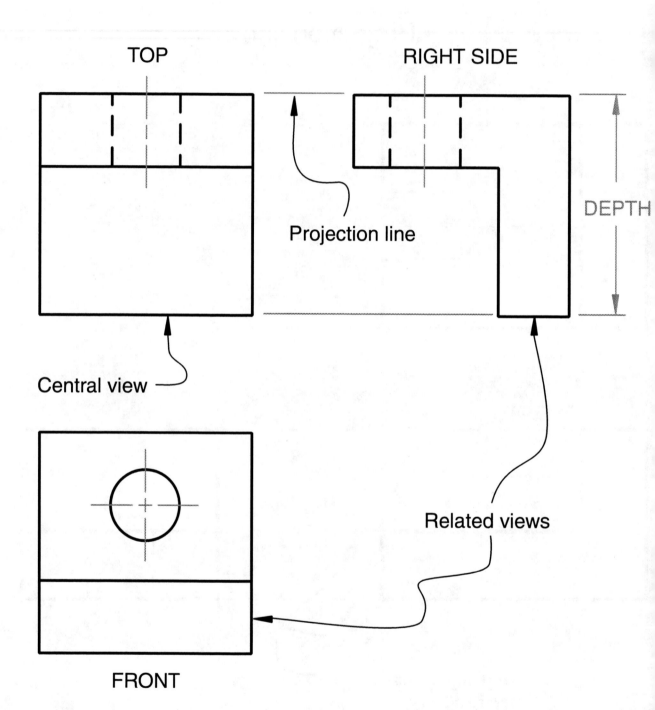

TOP

RIGHT SIDE

Projection line

DEPTH

Central view

Related views

FRONT

TM-113   Figure 8.22
Standard Arrangement of the Six Principal Views for Third- and First-Angle Projection

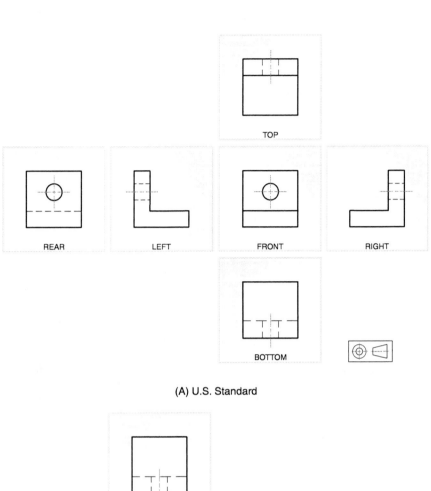

(A) U.S. Standard

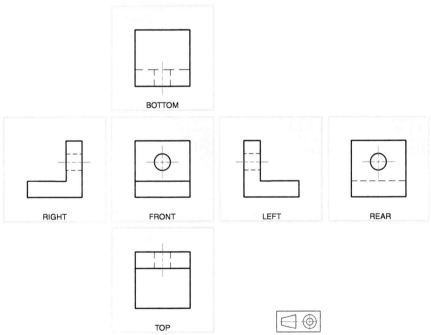

(B) European Standard

TM-114   Figure 8.27
Alphabet of Lines

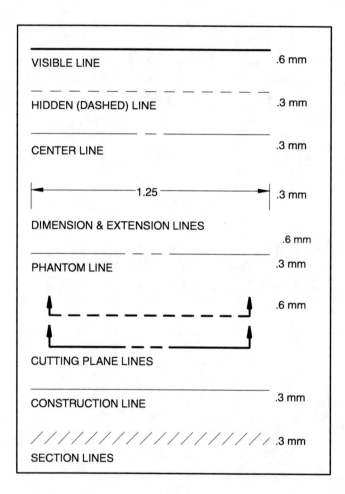

VISIBLE LINE	.6 mm
HIDDEN (DASHED) LINE	.3 mm
CENTER LINE	.3 mm
DIMENSION & EXTENSION LINES	.3 mm
PHANTOM LINE	.6 mm / .3 mm
CUTTING PLANE LINES	.6 mm
CONSTRUCTION LINE	.3 mm
SECTION LINES	.3 mm

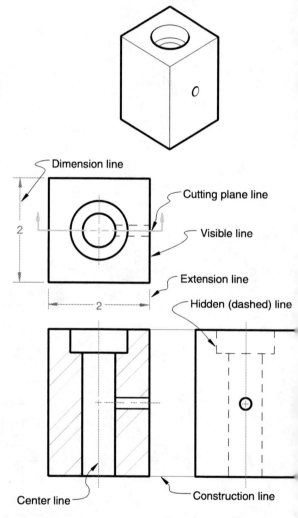

Dimension line

Cutting plane line

Visible line

Extension line

Hidden (dashed) line

Center line

Construction line

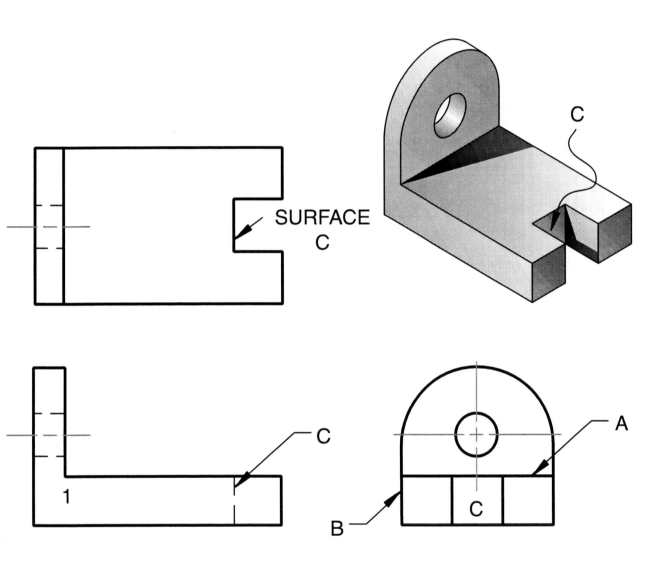

SURFACE
C

C

1

C

A

B

C

TM-116　Figure 8.34
Steps to Center and Create a Three-View Multiview Drawing on an A-Size Sheet

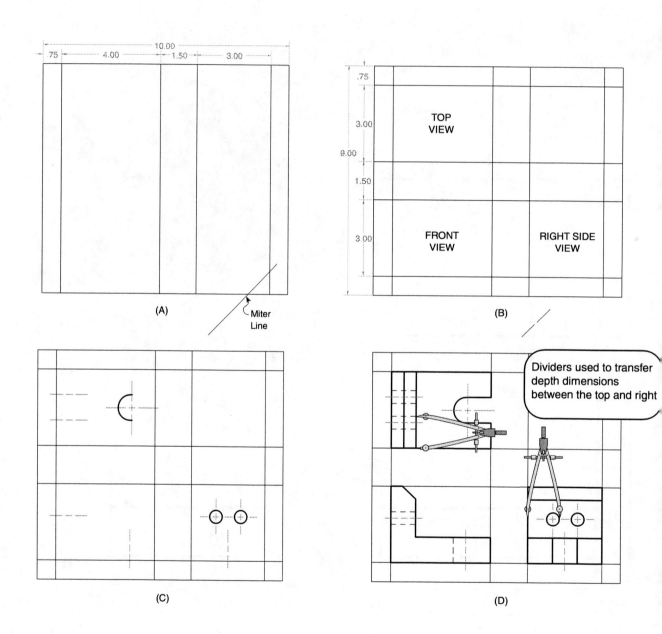

(A)

Miter Line

(B)

(C)

(D)

Dividers used to transfer depth dimensions between the top and right

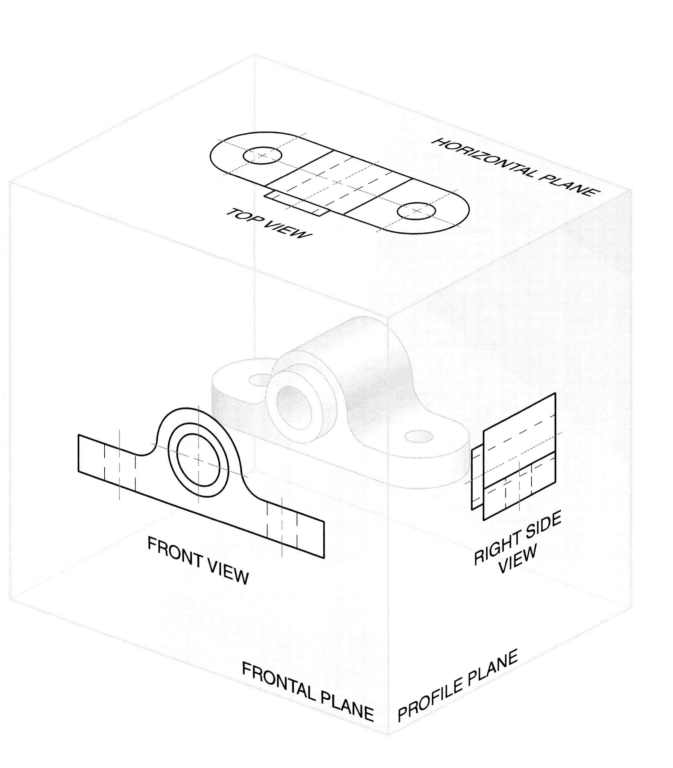

TOP VIEW

HORIZONTAL PLANE

FRONT VIEW

RIGHT SIDE VIEW

FRONTAL PLANE

PROFILE PLANE

TM-118 Figure 8.40
Poor Orientation

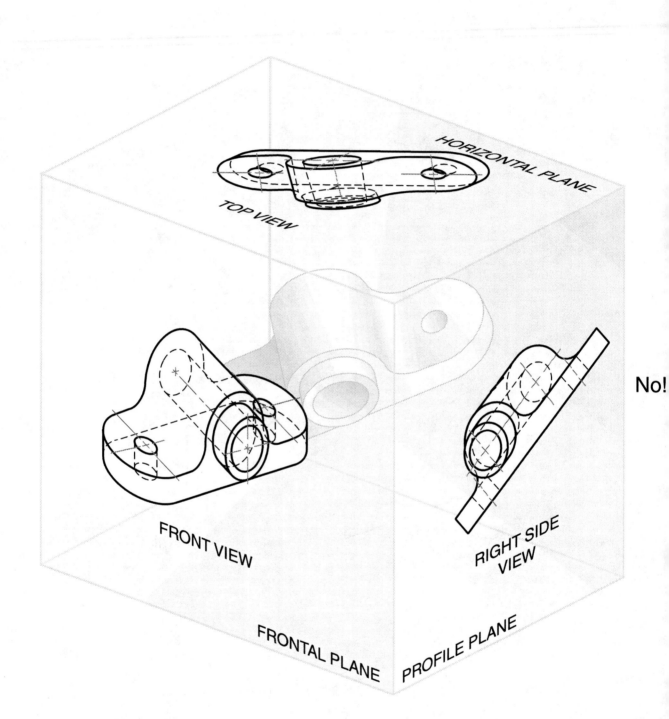

TOP VIEW

HORIZONTAL PLANE

No!

FRONT VIEW

RIGHT SIDE VIEW

FRONTAL PLANE

PROFILE PLANE

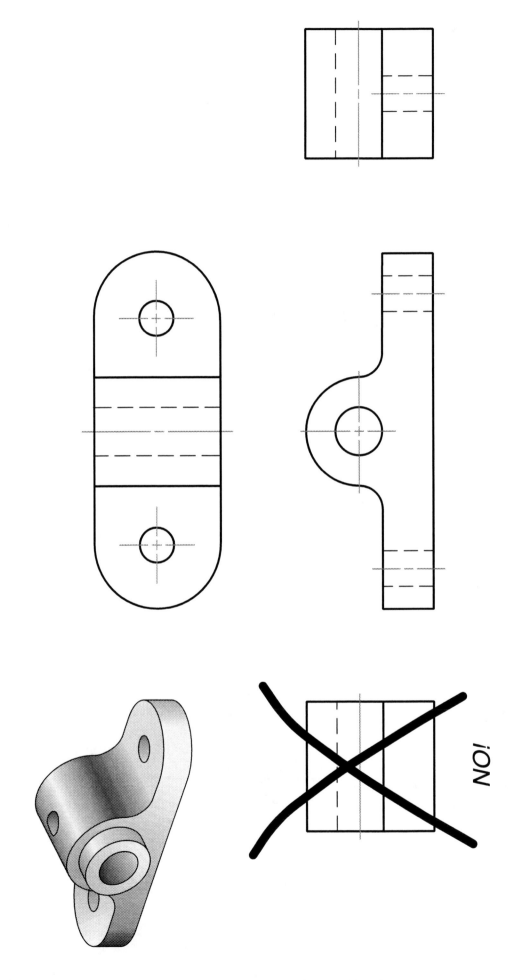

NO!

TM-120   Figure 8.46
Fundamental Views of Surfaces

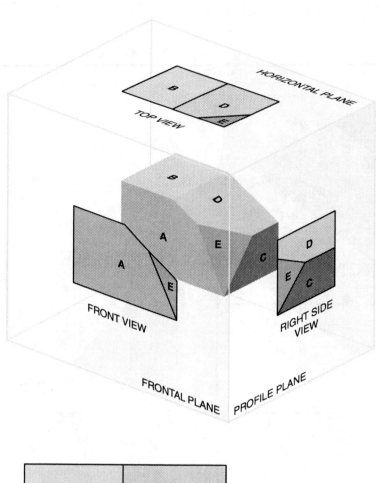

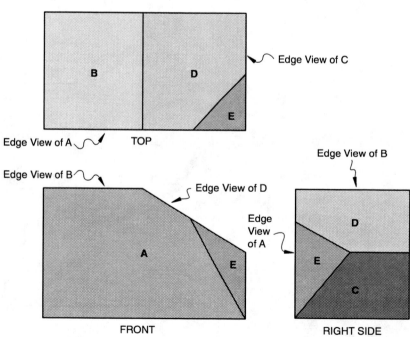

TM-121   Figure 8.48
Rule of Configuration of Planes

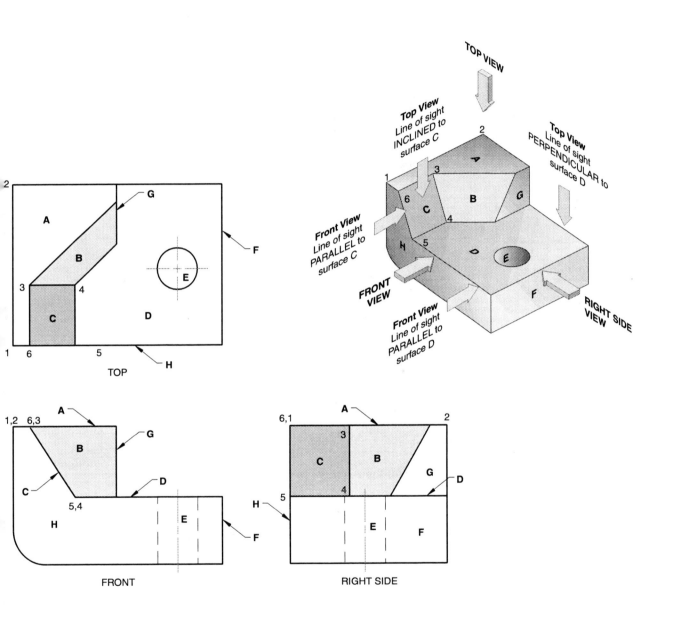

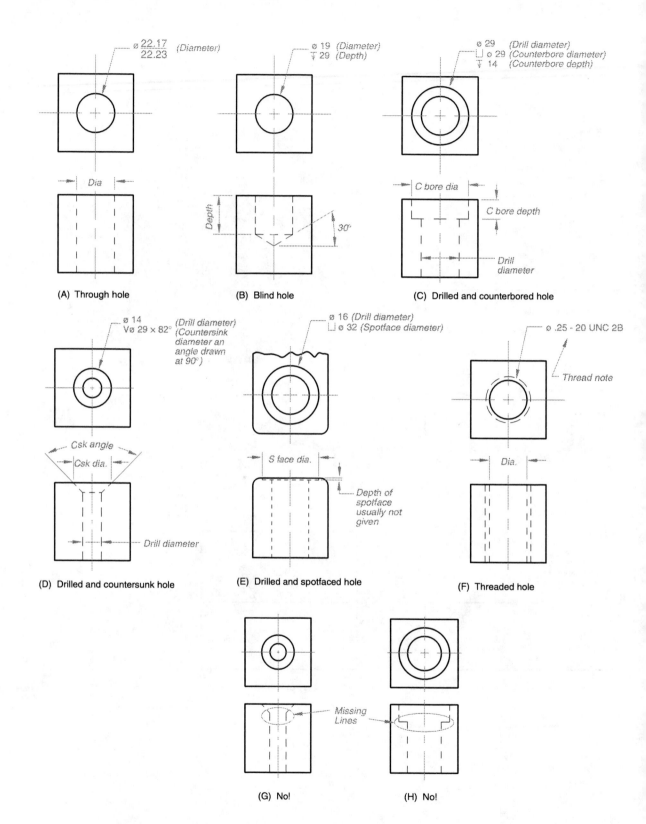

(A) Through hole

(B) Blind hole

(C) Drilled and counterbored hole

(D) Drilled and countersunk hole

(E) Drilled and spotfaced hole

(F) Threaded hole

(G) No!

(H) No!

TM-123 Figure 8.58
Examples of Representations of Filleted and Rounded Corners

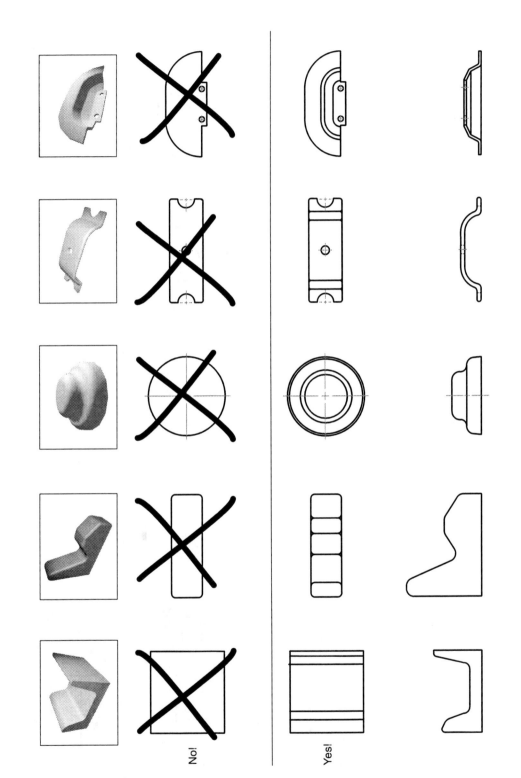

TM-124   Figure 8.61
Runouts

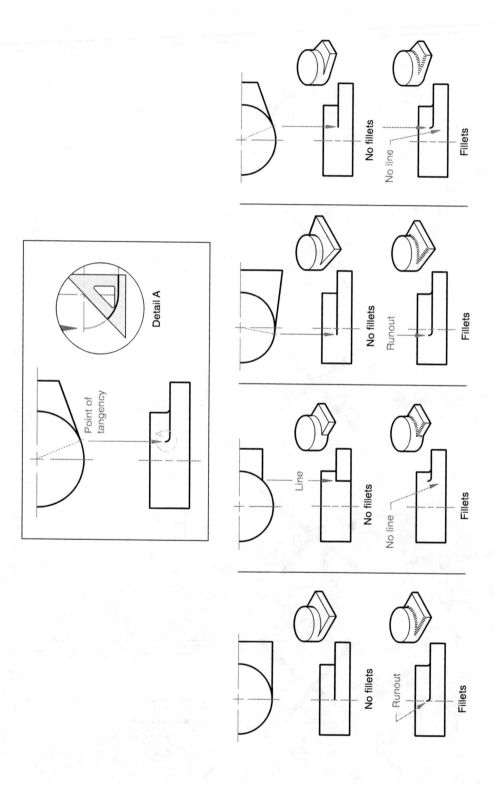

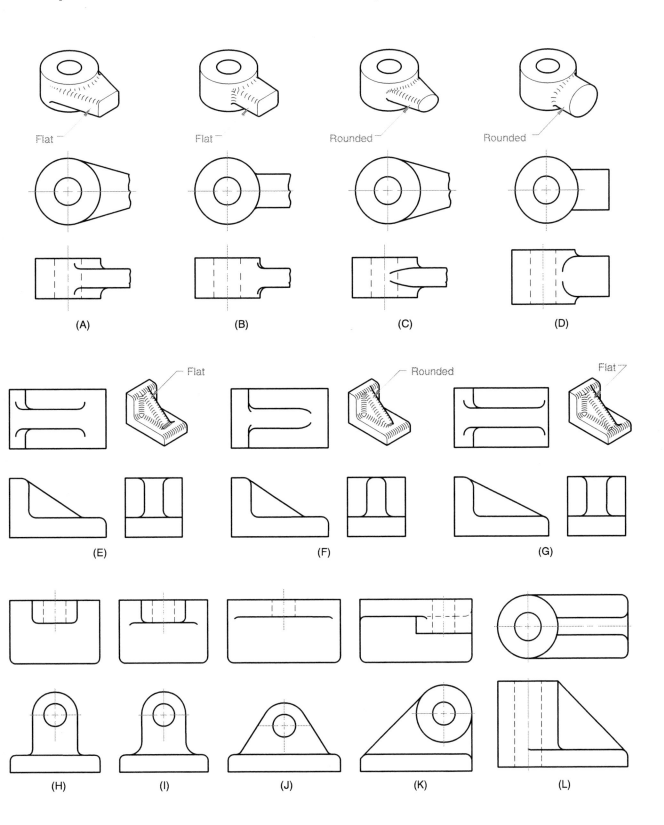

Flat

Flat

Rounded

Rounded

(A)

(B)

(C)

(D)

Flat

Rounded

Flat

(E)

(F)

(G)

(H)

(I)

(J)

(K)

(L)

TM-126   Figure 8.66
Representing the Intersection of Two Cylinders

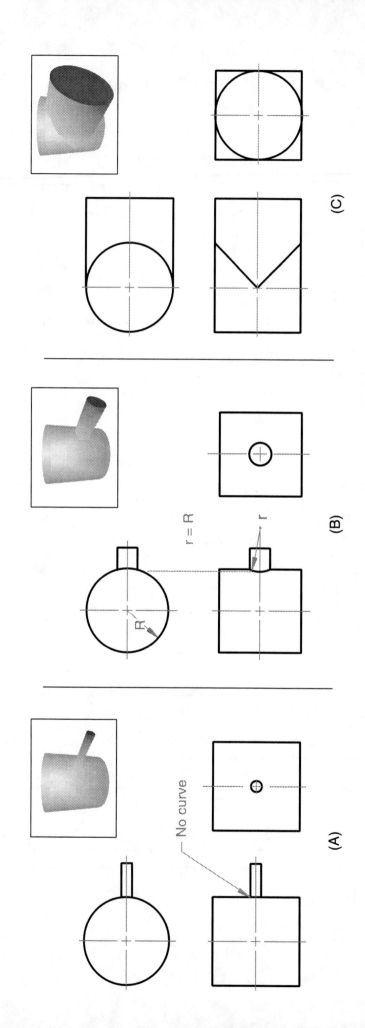

TM-127   Figure 8.67
Representing the Intersection between a Cylinder and a Prism

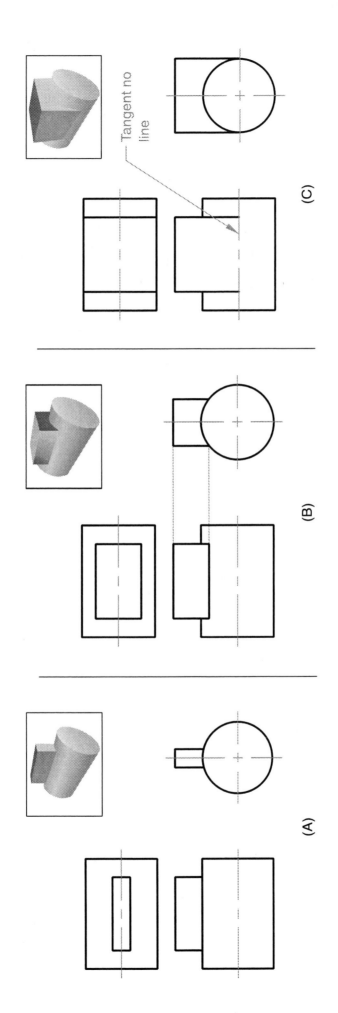

TM-128   Figure 8.68
Representing the Intersection between a Cylinder and a Hole

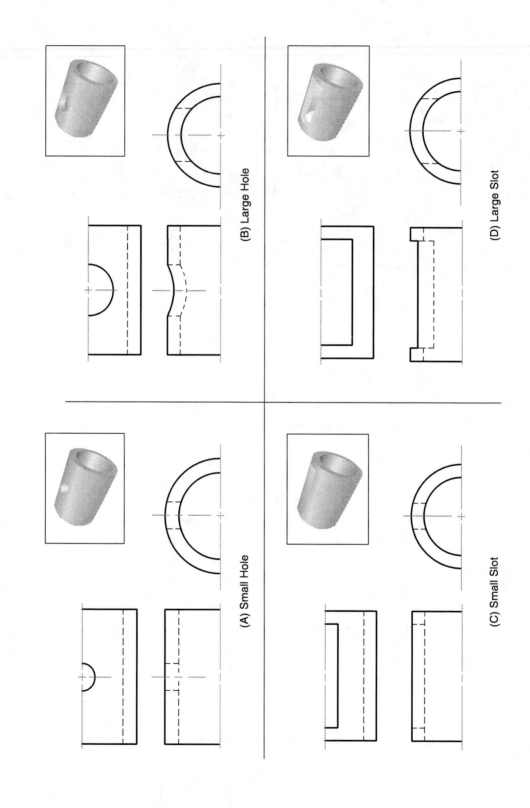

(A) Small Hole

(B) Large Hole

(C) Small Slot

(D) Large Slot

TM-129   Figure 8.74
Similar-Shaped Surfaces

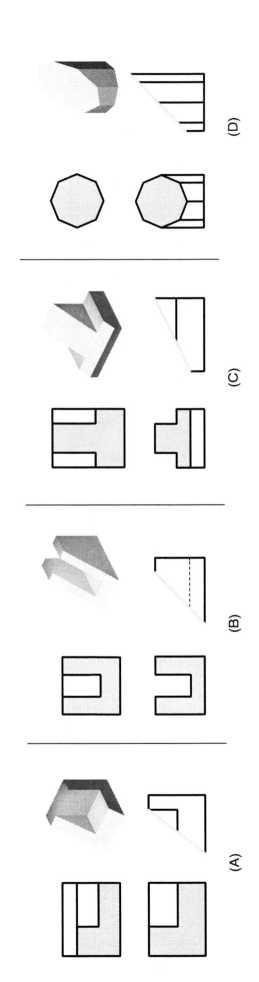

(A)　　(B)　　(C)　　(D)

TM-130   Figure 8.75
Surface Labeling

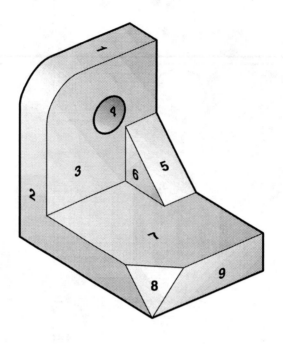

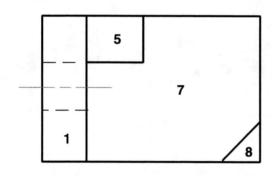

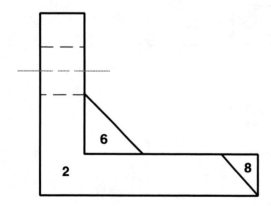

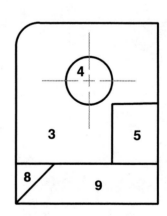

TM-131   Figure 8.77
Numbering the Isometric Pictorial and the Multiviews to Help Visualize an Object

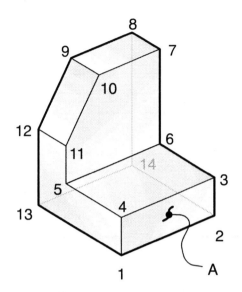

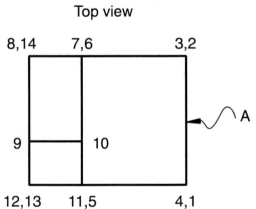

Top view

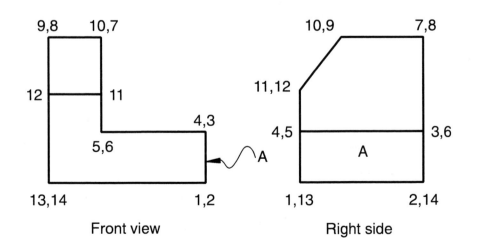

Front view   Right side

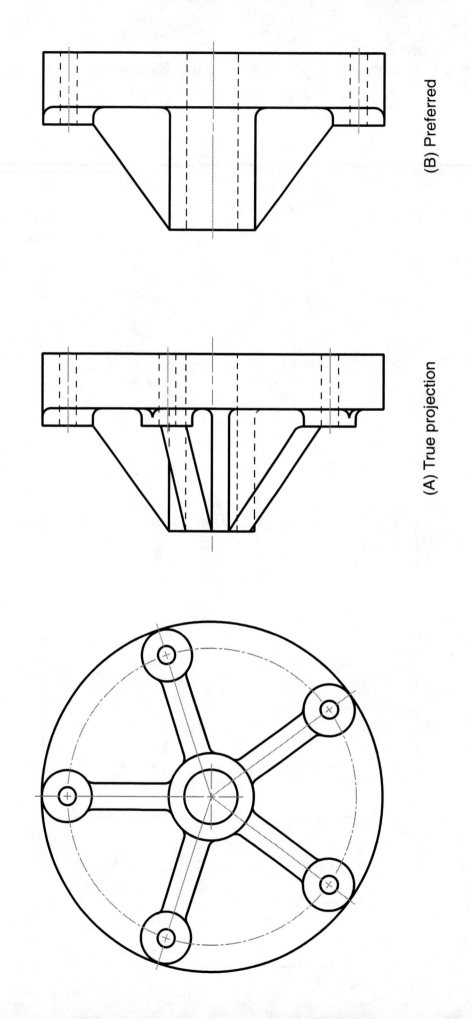

TM-132   Figure 8.85
Revolution Convention Used to Simplify the Representation of Ribs and Webs

(B) Preferred

(A) True projection

© The McGraw-Hill Companies, Inc., 1997

TM-133   Figure 8.86
Revolution Convention Used on Objects with Bolt Circles to Eliminate Hidden Lines and Improve Visualization

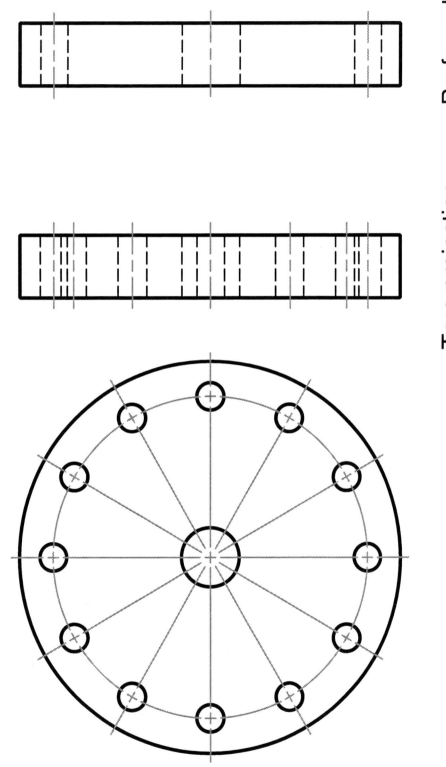

True projection

Preferred

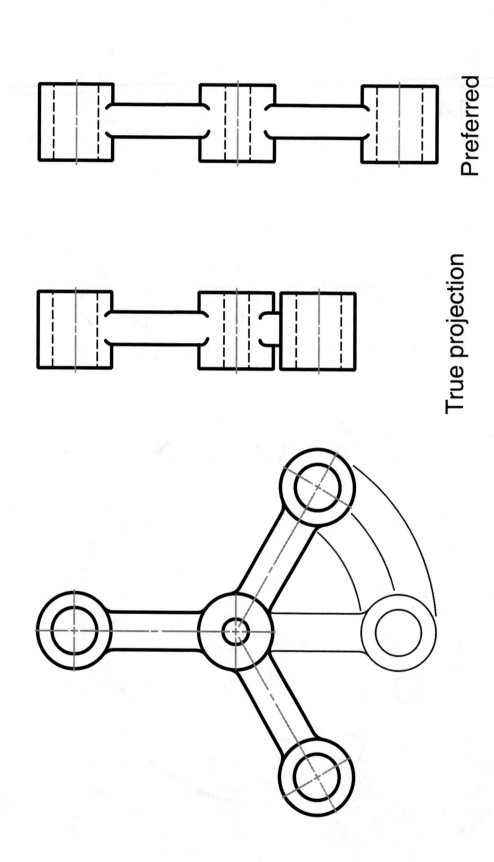

Preferred

True projection

TM-135   Figure 9.2
Projection Techniques: Multiview, Axonometric, Oblique, and Perspective

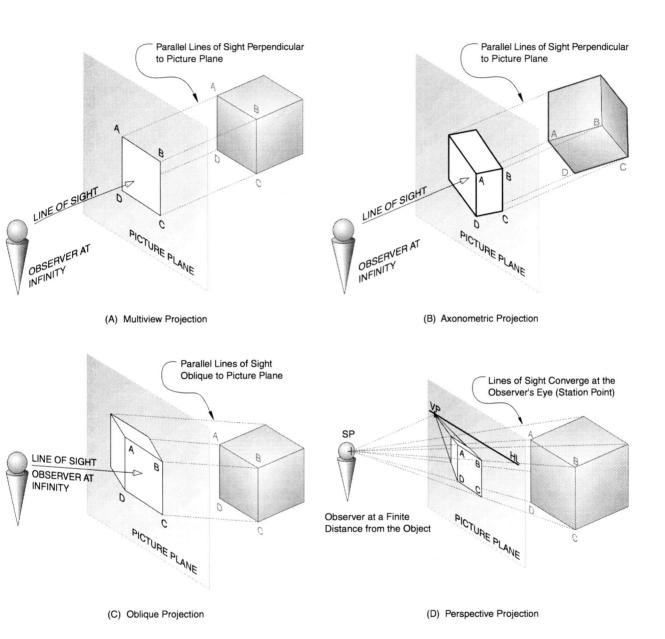

(A) Multiview Projection

(B) Axonometric Projection

(C) Oblique Projection

(D) Perspective Projection

TM-136   Figure 9.3
Angles That Determine the Type of Axonometric Drawing Produced

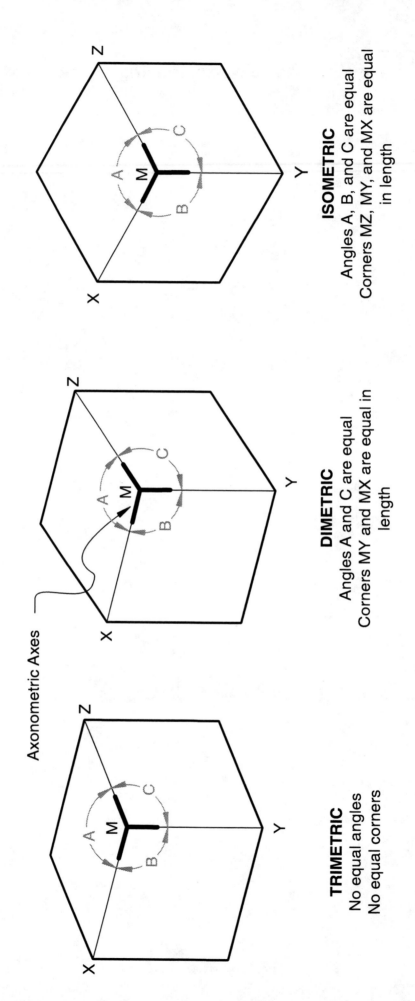

TRIMETRIC
No equal angles
No equal corners

Axonometric Axes

DIMETRIC
Angles A and C are equal
Corners MY and MX are equal in
length

ISOMETRIC
Angles A, B, and C are equal
Corners MZ, MY, and MX are equal
in length

TM-137   Figure 9.5
Theory of Isometric Projection

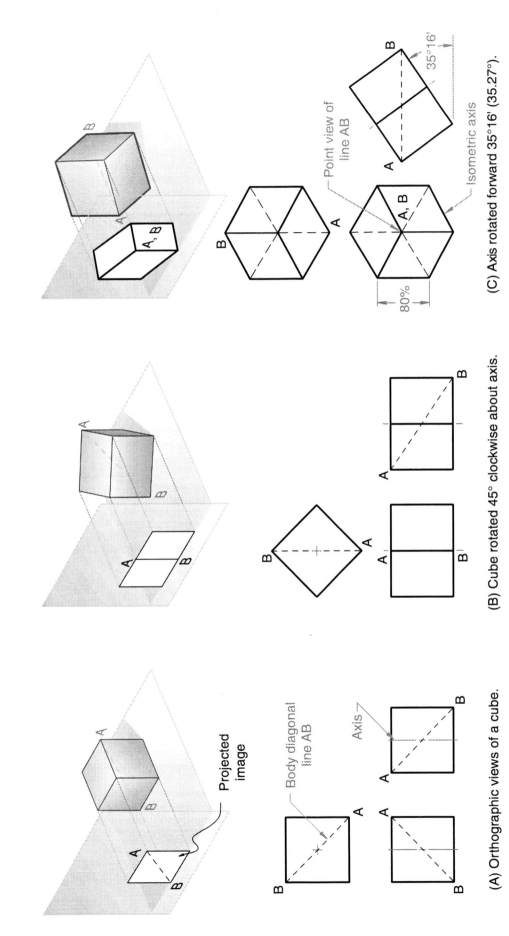

Projected image

(A) Orthographic views of a cube.

Body diagonal line AB

Axis

(B) Cube rotated 45° clockwise about axis.

Point view of line AB

Isometric axis

80%

35°16'

(C) Axis rotated forward 35°16' (35.27°).

Positions of Isometric Axes and Their Effect on the View Created

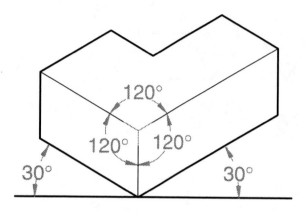

(A) Regular isometric

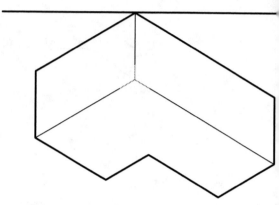

(B) Reversed axis isometric

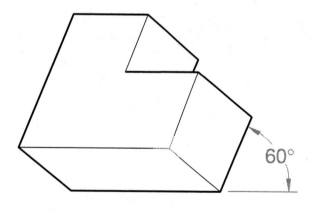

(C) Long axis isometric

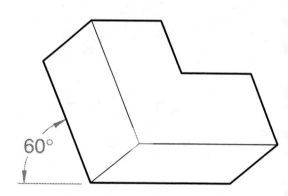

(D) Long axis isometric

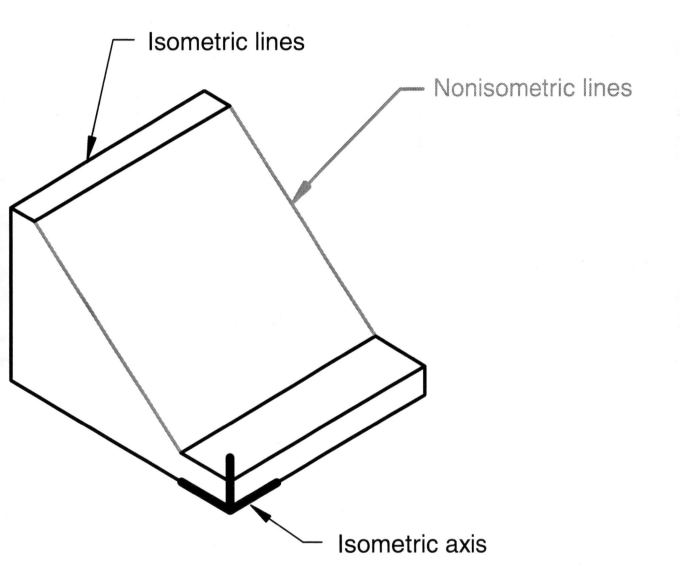

Isometric lines

Nonisometric lines

Isometric axis

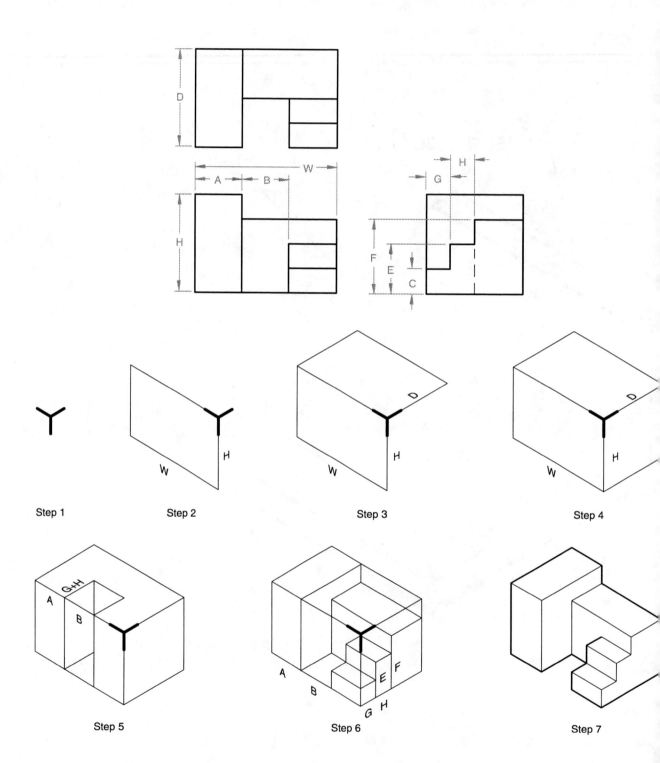

Step 1   Step 2   Step 3   Step 4

Step 5   Step 6   Step 7

TM-141   Figure 9.18
Constructing an Isometric Drawing Having Nonisometric Lines

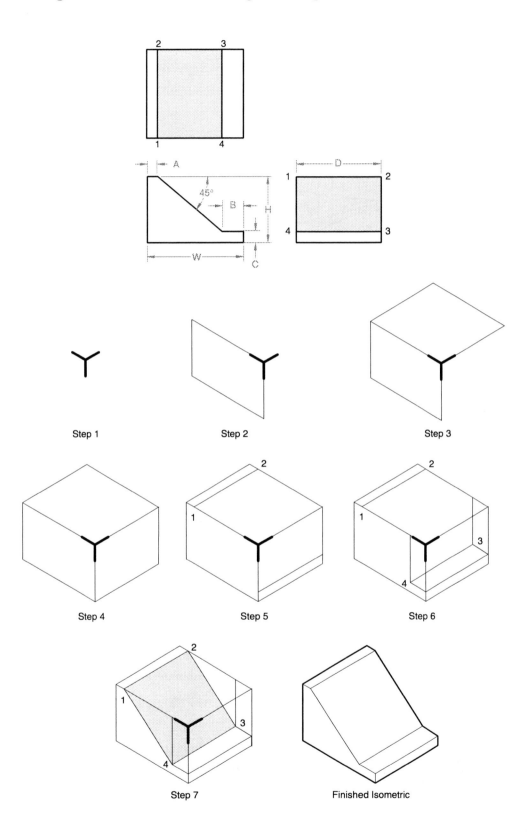

Step 1

Step 2

Step 3

Step 4

Step 5

Step 6

Step 7

Finished Isometric

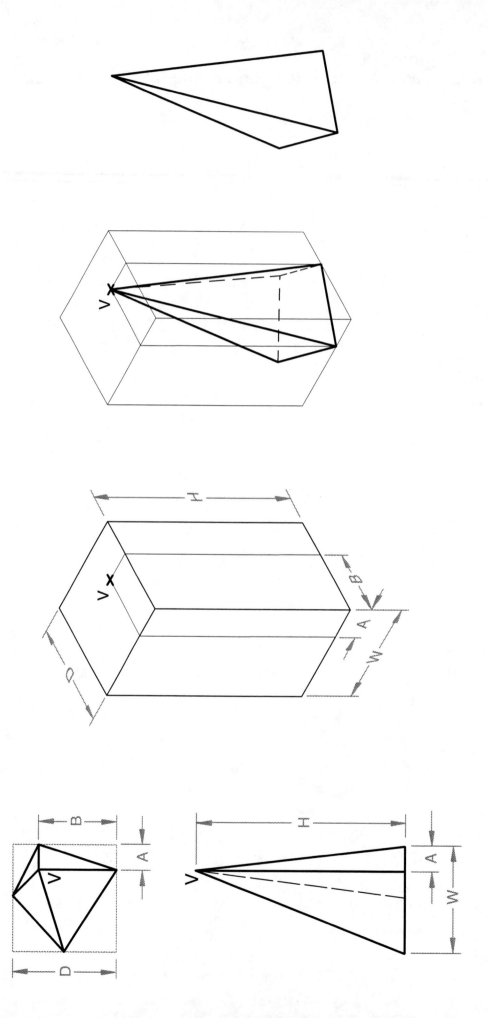

Four-Center Ellipses Drawn on the Three Faces of an Isometric Cube

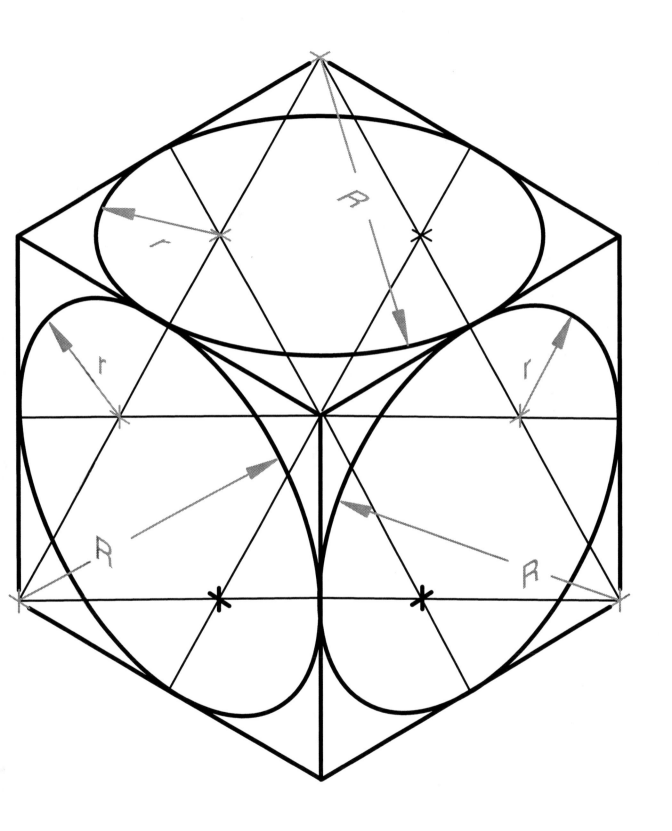

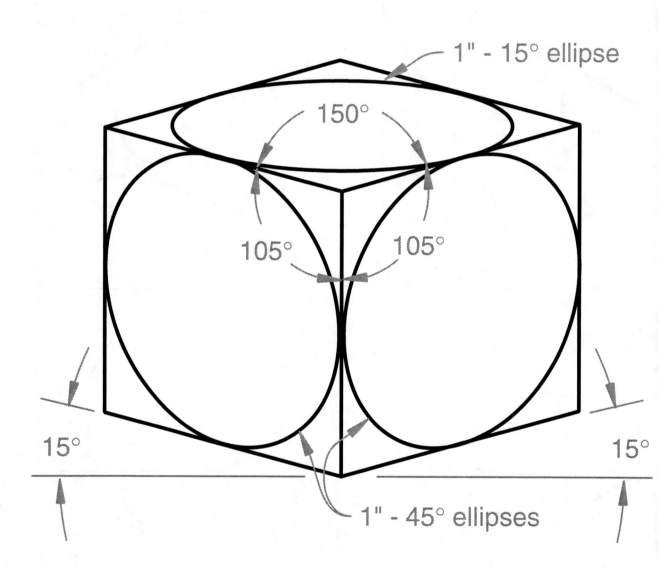

1" - 15° ellipse

150°

105°   105°

15°

15°

1" - 45° ellipses

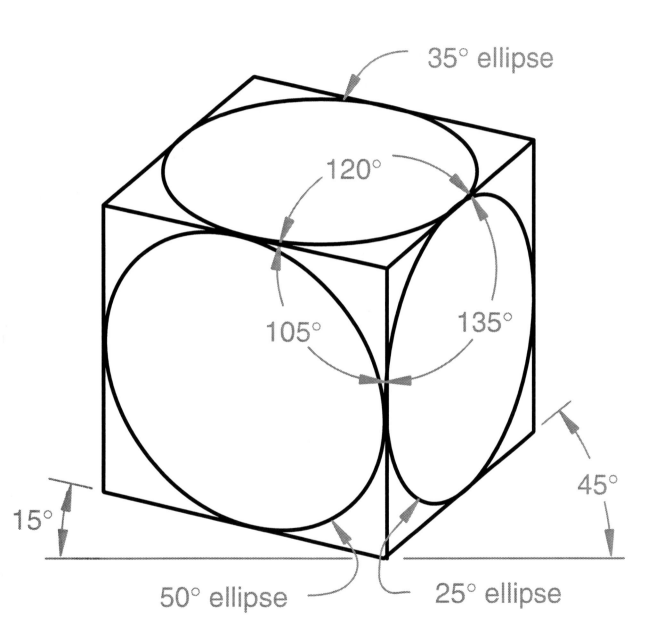

35° ellipse

120°

105°

135°

15°

45°

50° ellipse

25° ellipse

TM-146   Figure 9.56
Oblique Drawing Angles

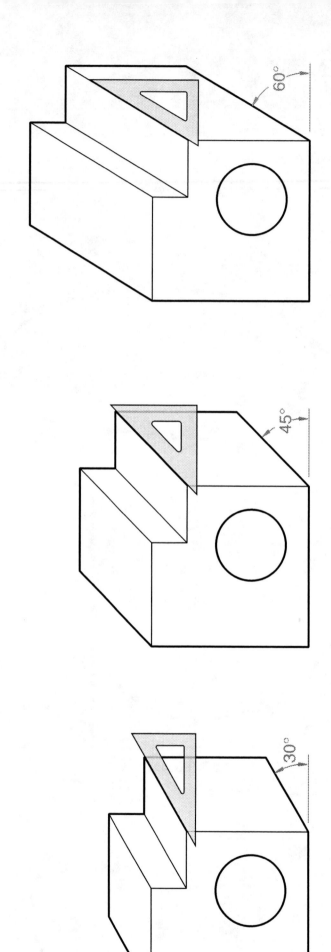

TM-147
Figure 9.59
Types of Oblique Drawings

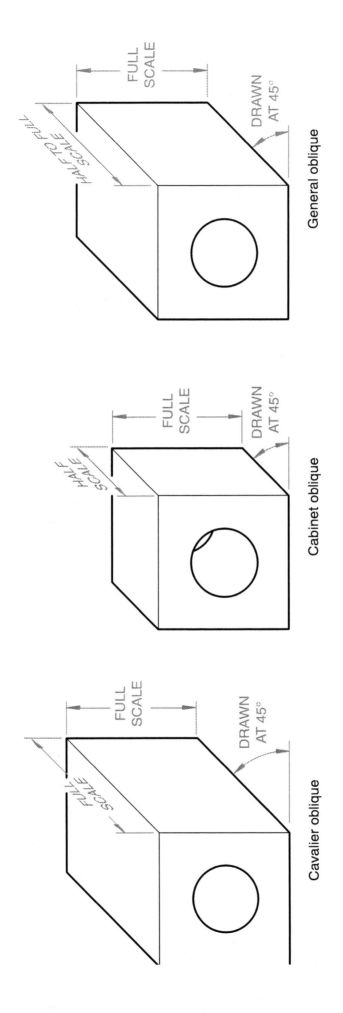

Cavalier oblique

Cabinet oblique

General oblique

TM-148 Figure 10.4
Perspective and Orthographic Profile Views of a Scene

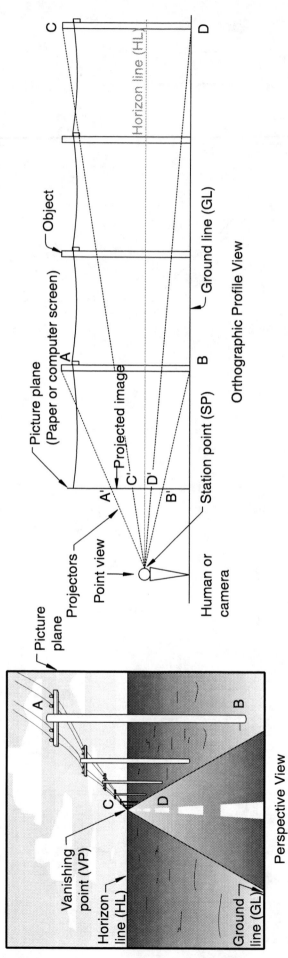

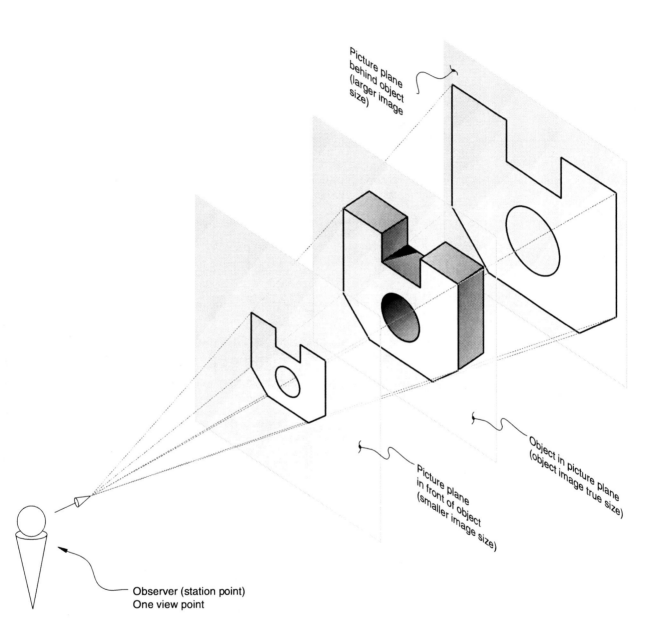

Picture plane
behind object
(larger image
size)

Object in picture plane
(object image true size)

Picture plane
in front of object
(smaller image size)

Observer (station point)
One view point

TM-150 Figure 10.6
Vanishing Point Position

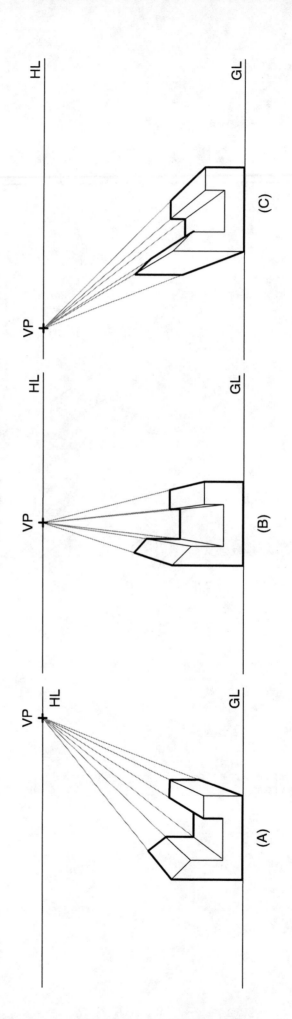

TM-151   Figure 10.7
Trace this photograph onto tracing paper to determine the vanishing point.

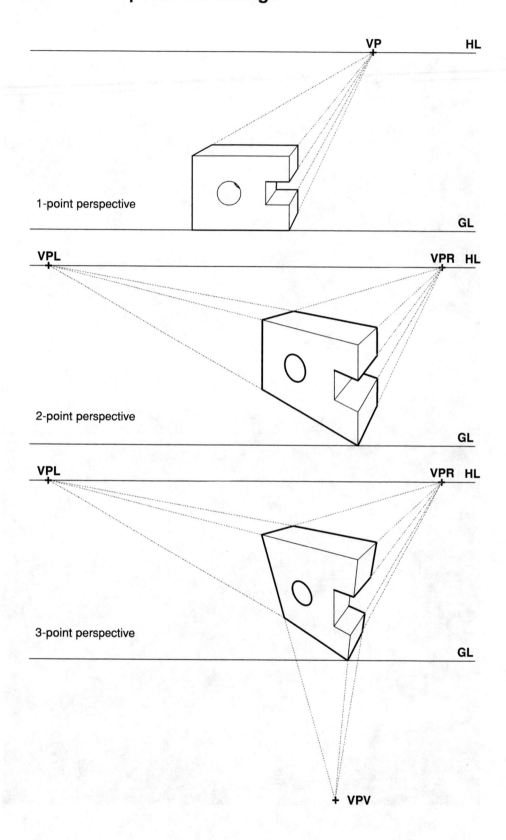

VP   HL

1-point perspective   GL

VPL   VPR HL

2-point perspective   GL

VPL   VPR HL

3-point perspective   GL

+ VPV

TM-153 Figure 11.1
Auxiliary View

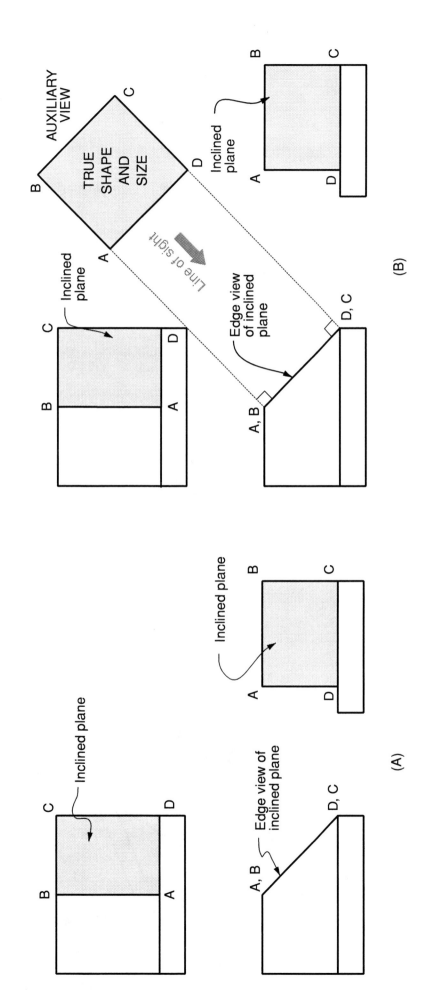

TM-154   Figure 11.2
Object in Glass Box, and Resulting Six Views When the Box Is Unfolded

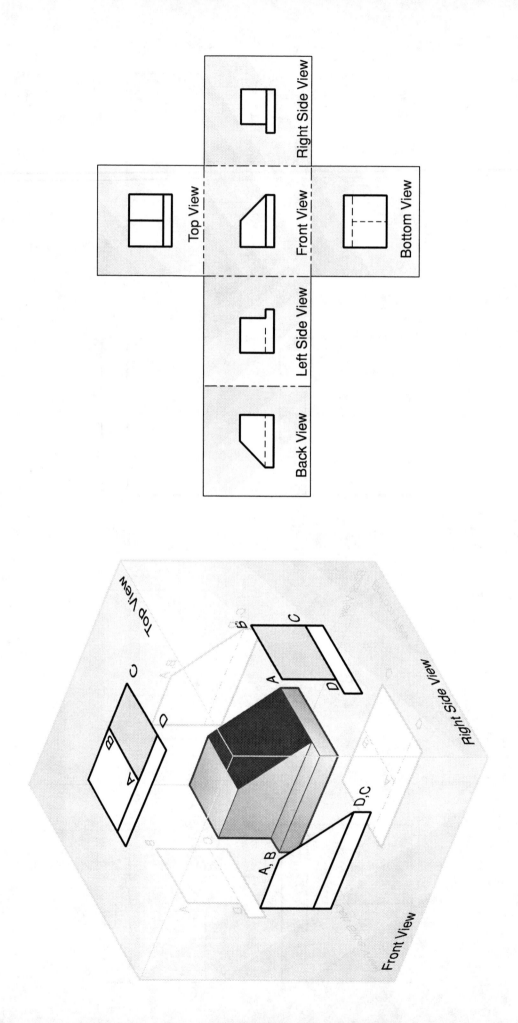

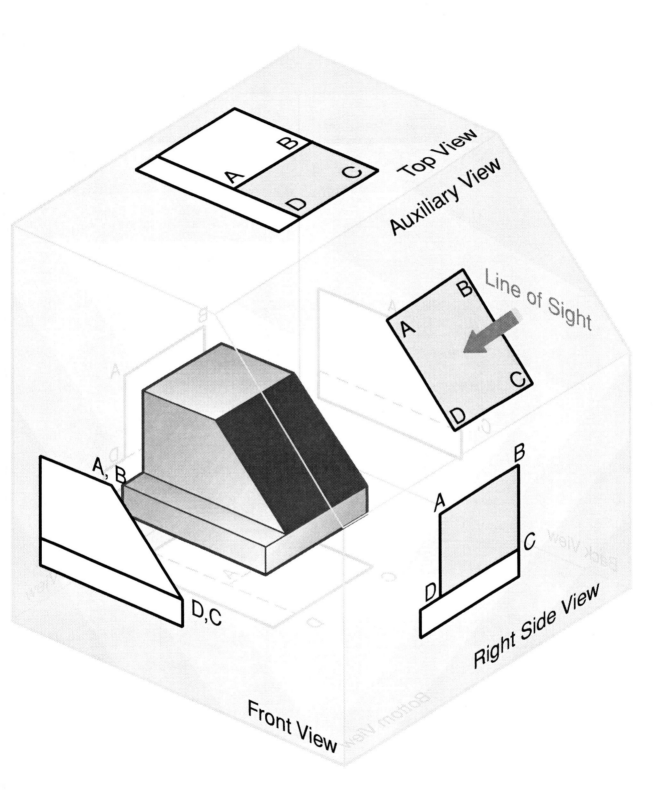

Top View

Auxiliary View

Line of Sight

Right Side View

Front View

TM-156   Figure 11.7
Primary, Secondary, and Tertiary Auxiliary Views

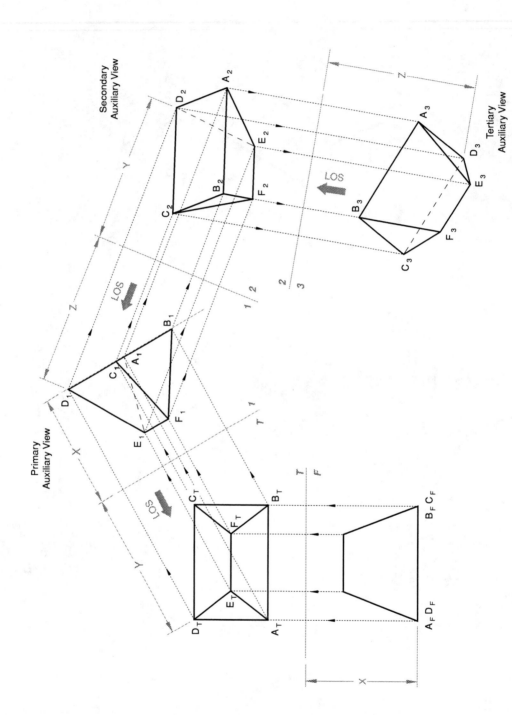

**A Full Auxiliary View, Including Hidden Lines, and a Partial Auxiliary
View with No Hidden Lines**

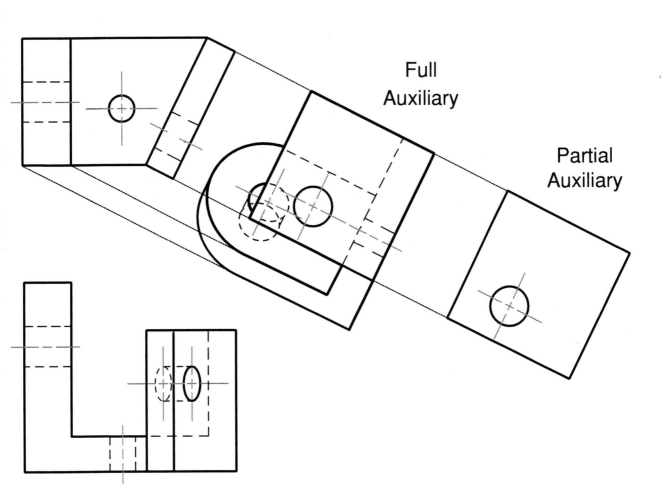

Full
Auxiliary

Partial
Auxiliary

TM-158   Figure 11.15
Constructing a View in a Specified Direction: Point View of a Line

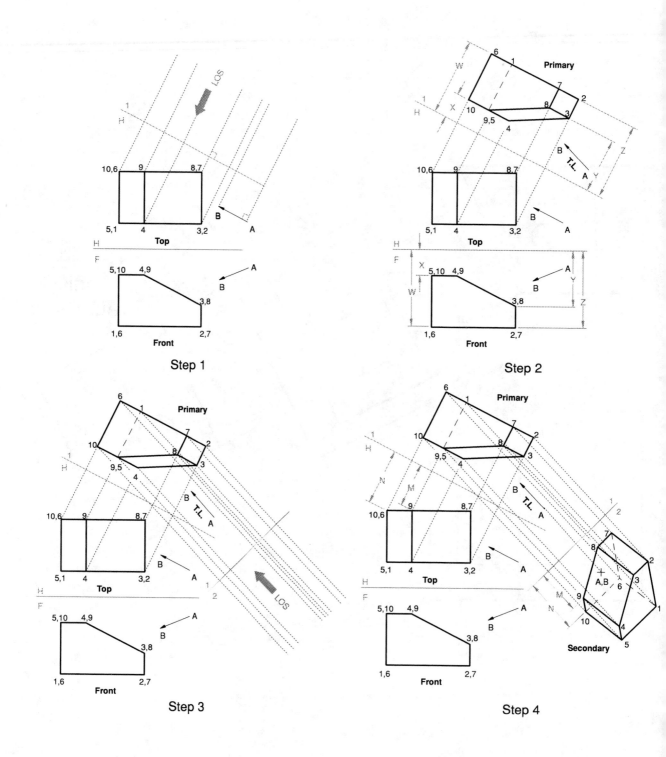

Step 1

Step 2

Step 3

Step 4

True Length of a Line: Auxiliary View Method

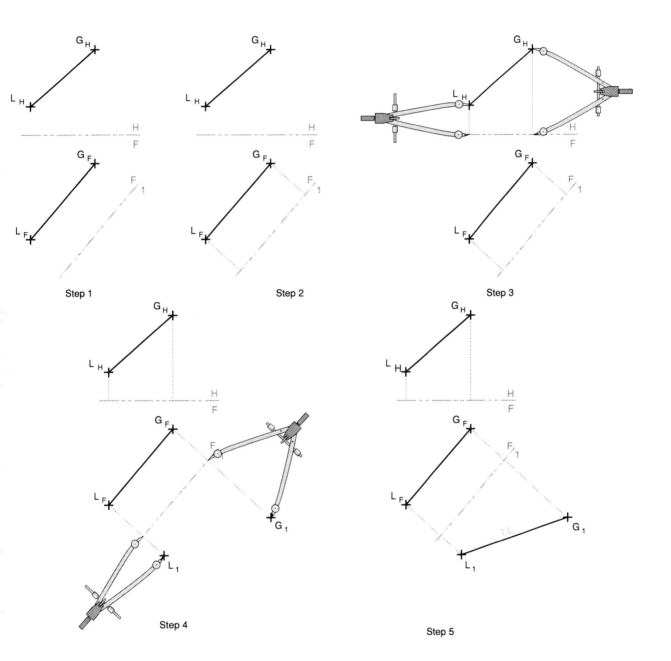

Step 1

Step 2

Step 3

Step 4

Step 5

TM-160 Figure 12.25
Graphical Representation of Planes

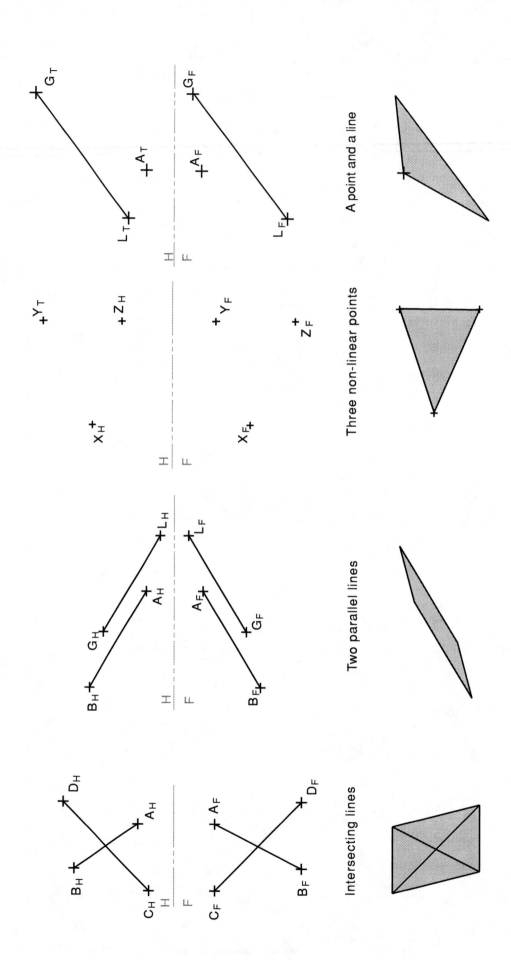

Intersecting lines

Two parallel lines

Three non-linear points

A point and a line

True Size of a Plane, Auxiliary View Method

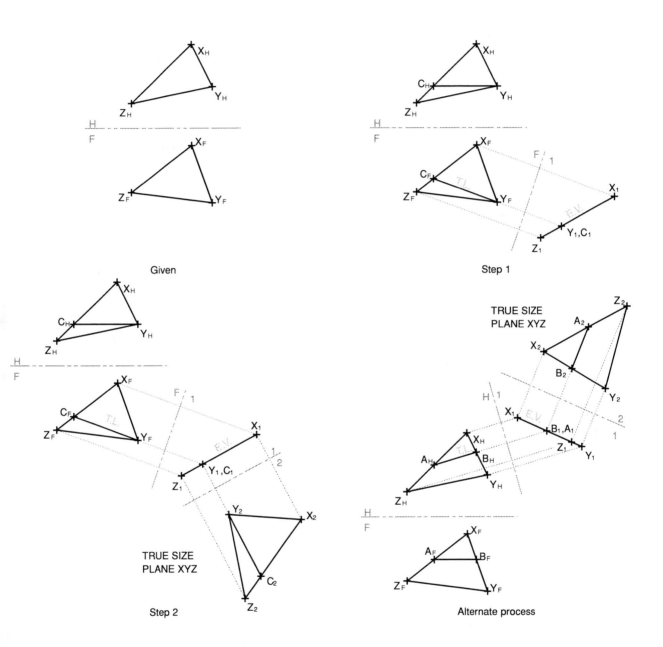

Given

Step 1

TRUE SIZE
PLANE XYZ

Step 2

TRUE SIZE
PLANE XYZ

Alternate process

TM-162 Figure 13.4
Visibility Demonstrated by Two Skew Lines

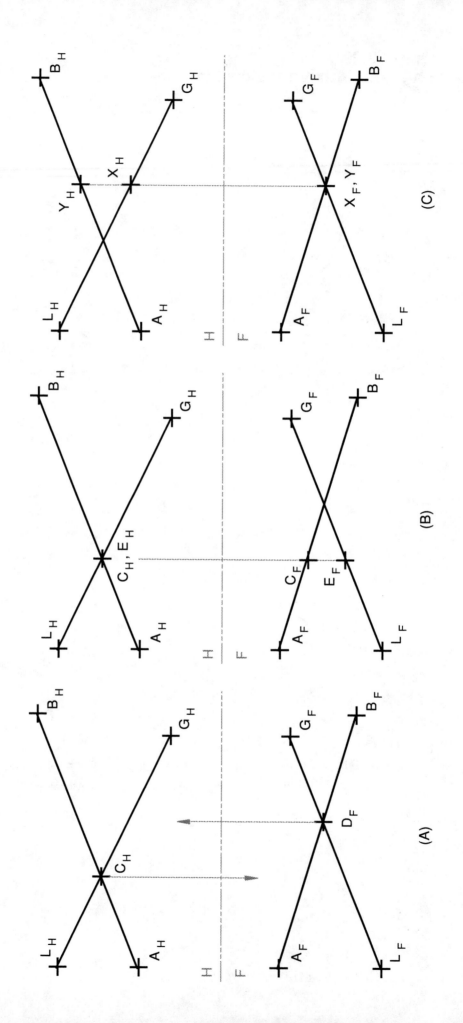

TM-163   Figure 13.6
Determining Visibility between Any Two Adjacent Views

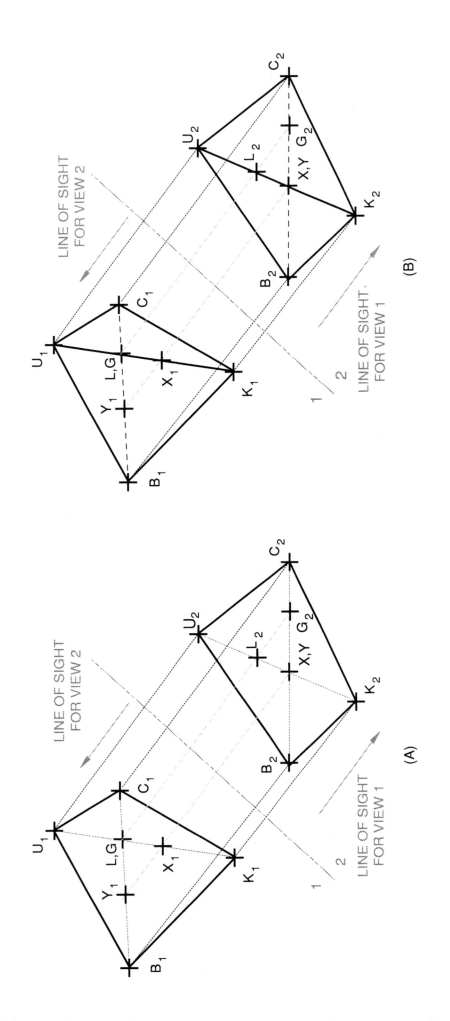

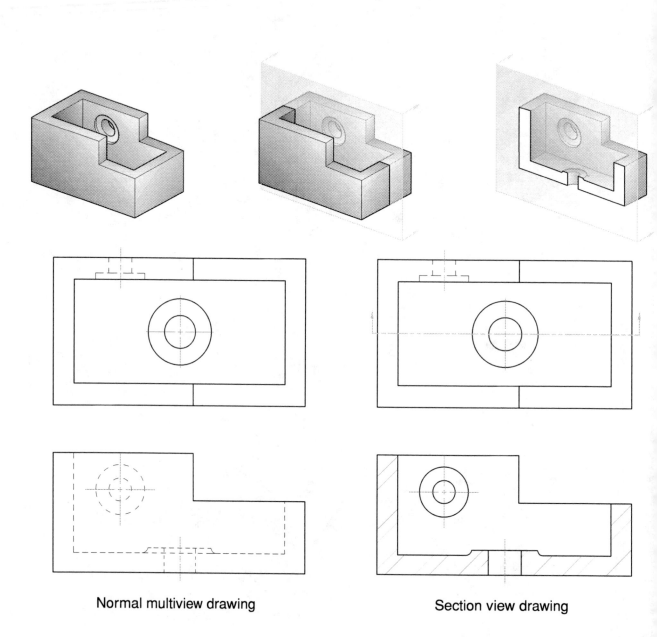

Normal multiview drawing　　　　　　Section view drawing

TM-165 Figure 14.3
Cutting Planes

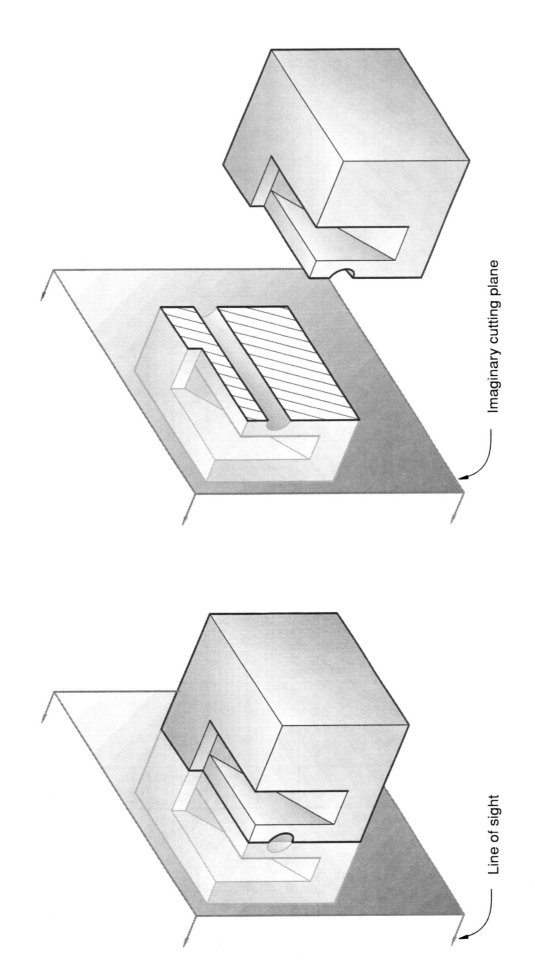

Imaginary cutting plane

Line of sight

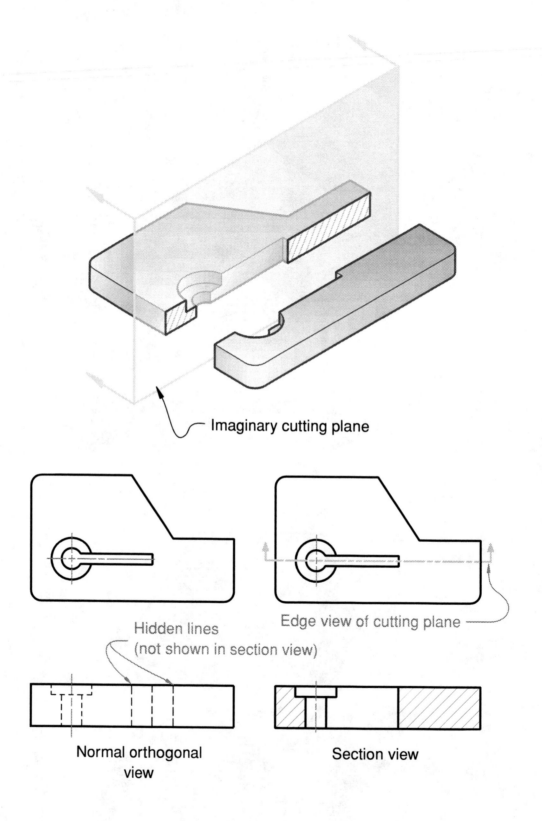

Imaginary cutting plane

Hidden lines
(not shown in section view)

Edge view of cutting plane

Normal orthogonal
view

Section view

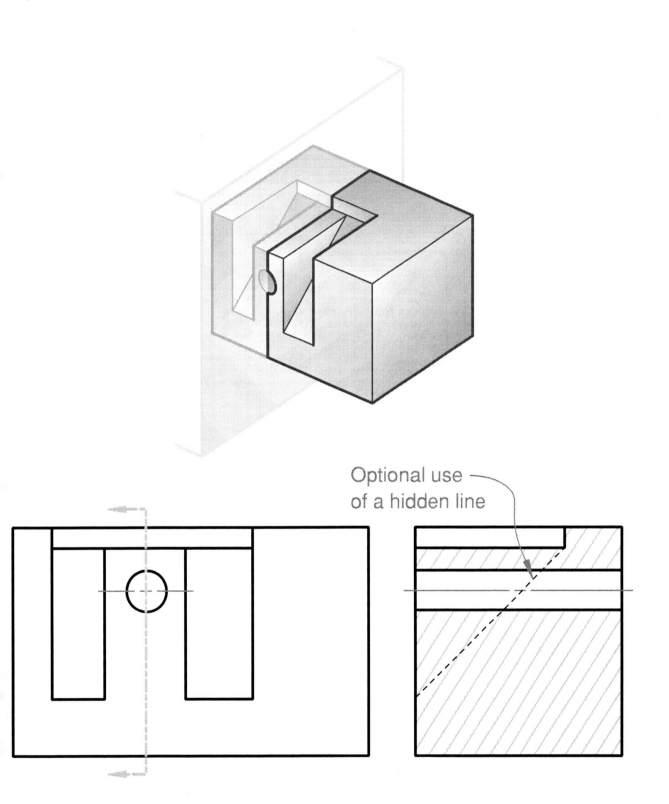

Optional use
of a hidden line

TM-168   Figure 14.25
Full Section View

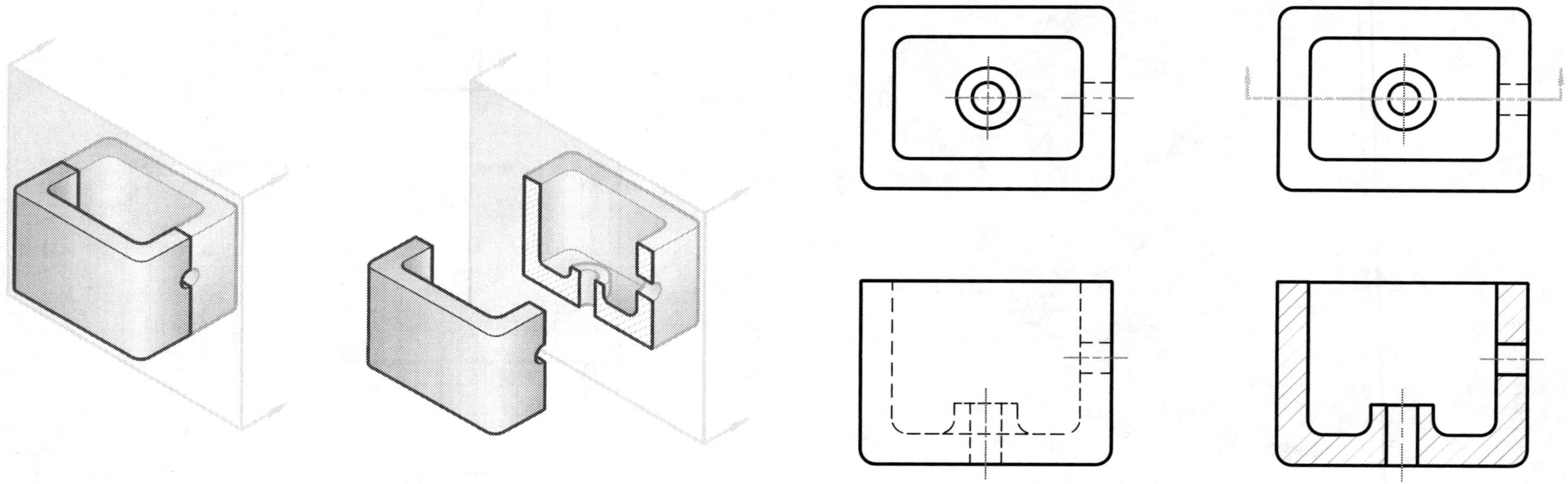

(A) Full section

(B) Standard multiview

(C) Full section view

© The McGraw-Hill Companies, Inc., 1997

TM-169 Figure 14.26
Half Section

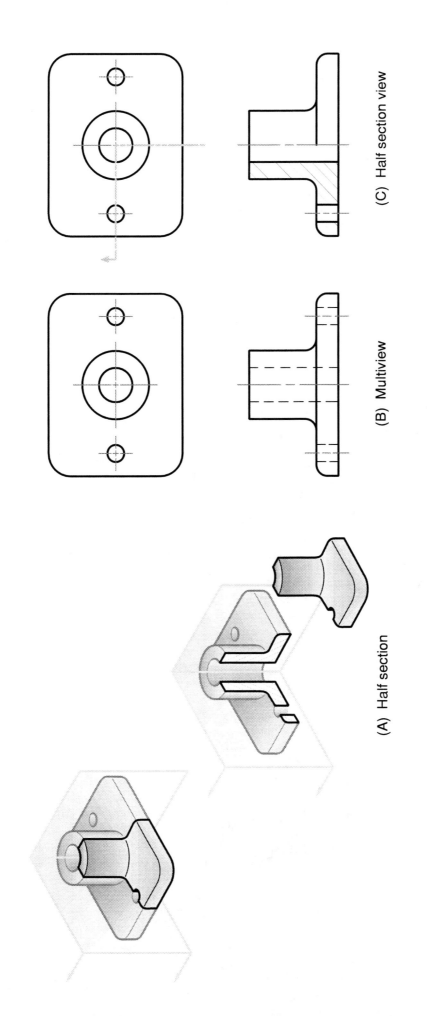

(C) Half section view

(B) Multiview

(A) Half section

TM-170   Figure 14.27
Broken-Out Section

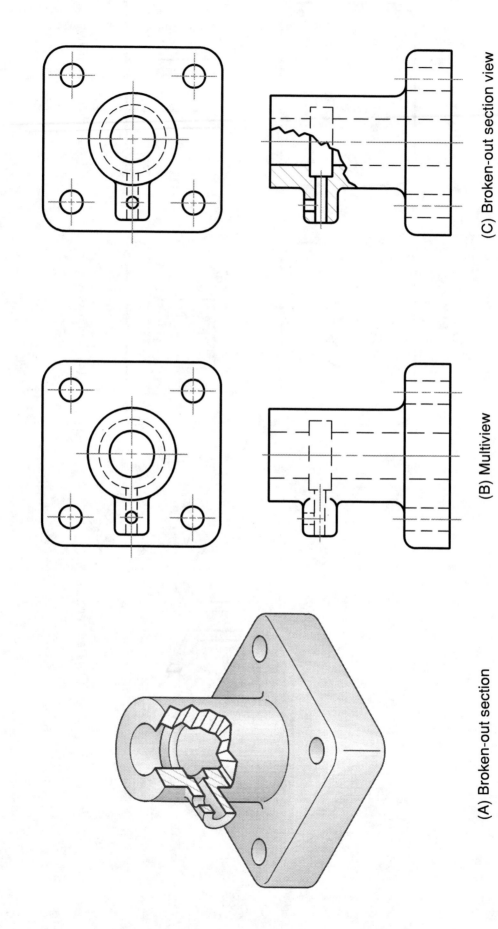

(C) Broken-out section view

(B) Multiview

(A) Broken-out section

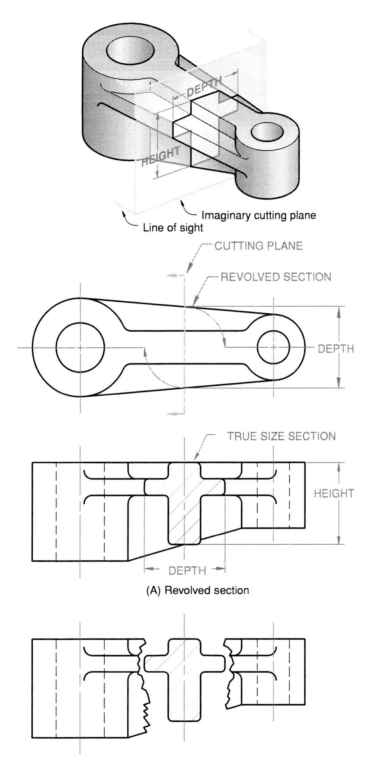

Imaginary cutting plane
Line of sight

CUTTING PLANE

REVOLVED SECTION

DEPTH

TRUE SIZE SECTION

HEIGHT

DEPTH

(A) Revolved section

(B) Revolved section; broken view

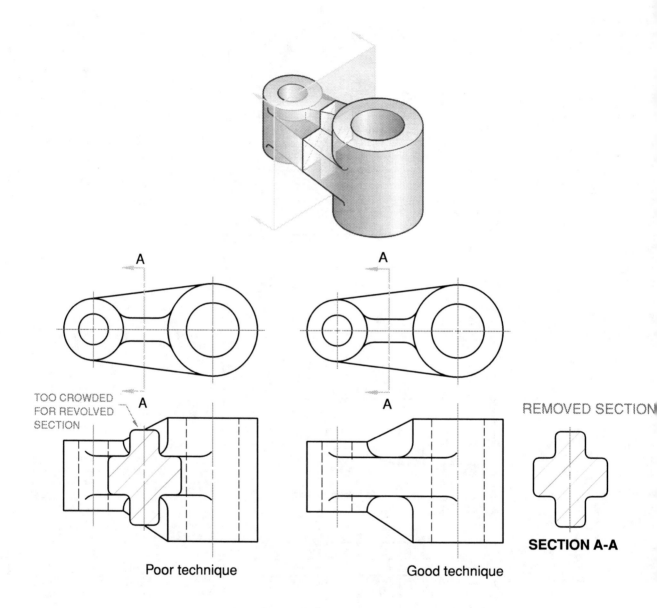

TOO CROWDED
FOR REVOLVED
SECTION

A

Poor technique

Good technique

REMOVED SECTION

SECTION A-A

Multiple Removed Section Views of a Connecting Rod Identified with Labels

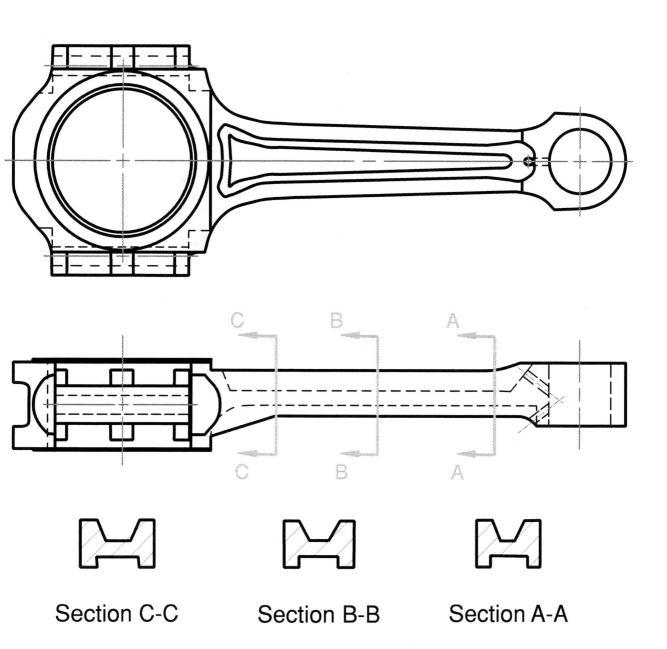

Section C-C   Section B-B   Section A-A

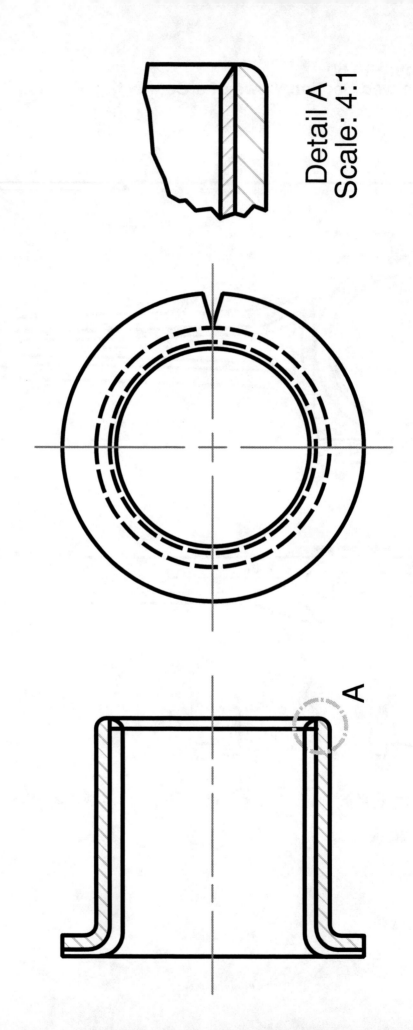

TM-174   Figure 14.31
Scaled Section View

Detail A
Scale: 4:1

A

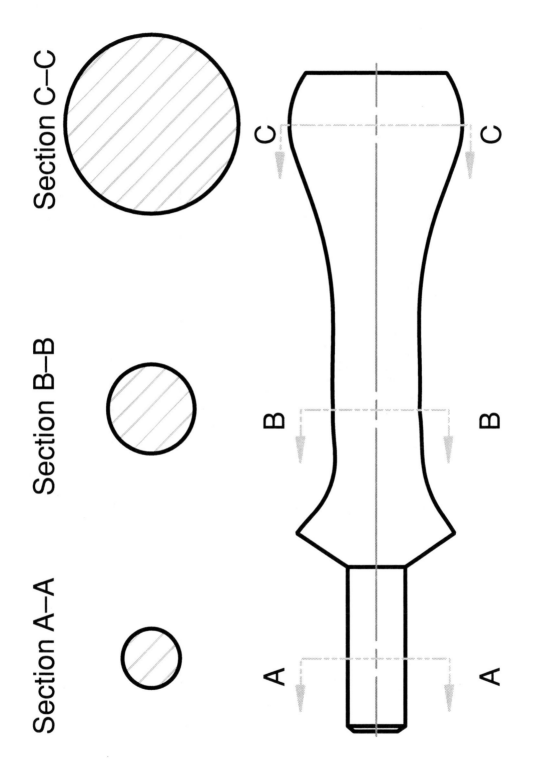

Section A–A

Section B–B

Section C–C

A

A

B

B

C

C

TM-176 Figure 14.33
Offset Section

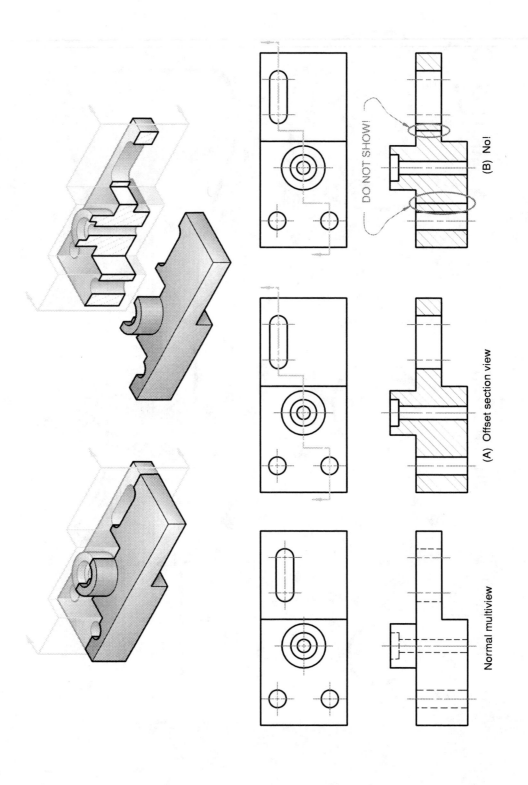

(A) Offset section view

(B) No!

DO NOT SHOW!

Normal multiview

TM-177 Figure 14.42
Conventional Practices for Webs in Section

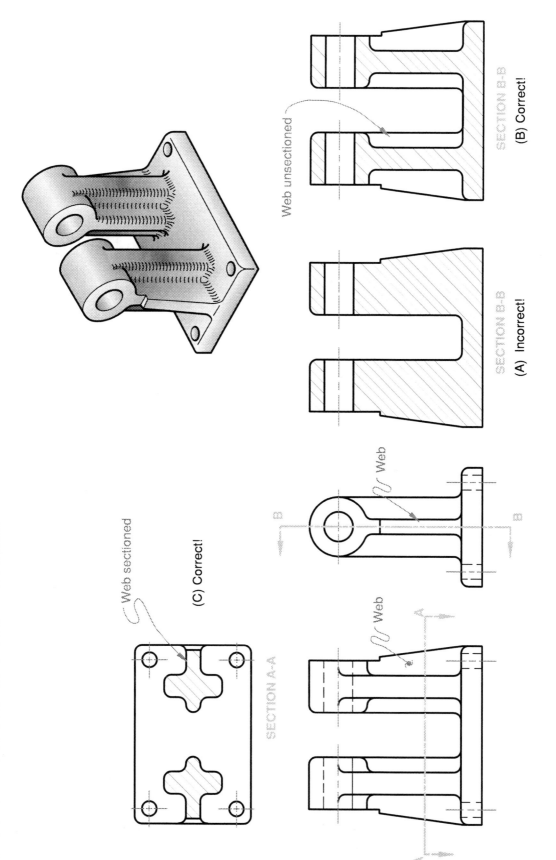

SECTION A-A

Web sectioned

(C) Correct!

Web

Web

SECTION B-B

(A) Incorrect!

SECTION B-B

(B) Correct!

Web unsectioned

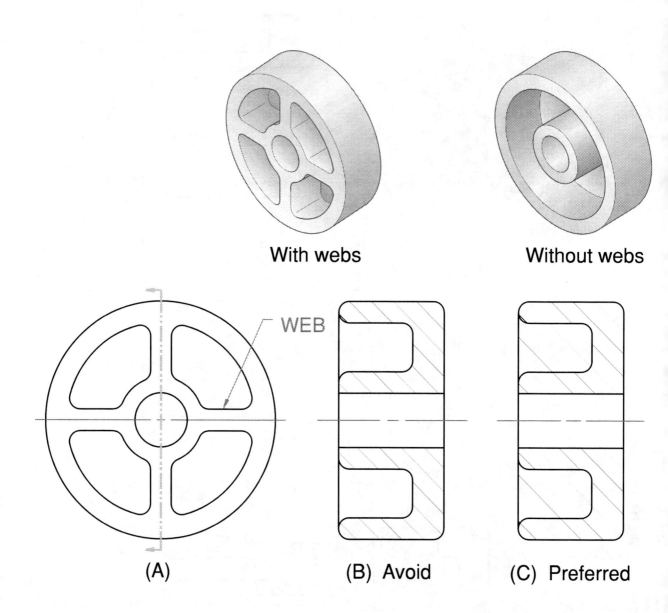

With webs

Without webs

WEB

(A)

(B) Avoid

(C) Preferred

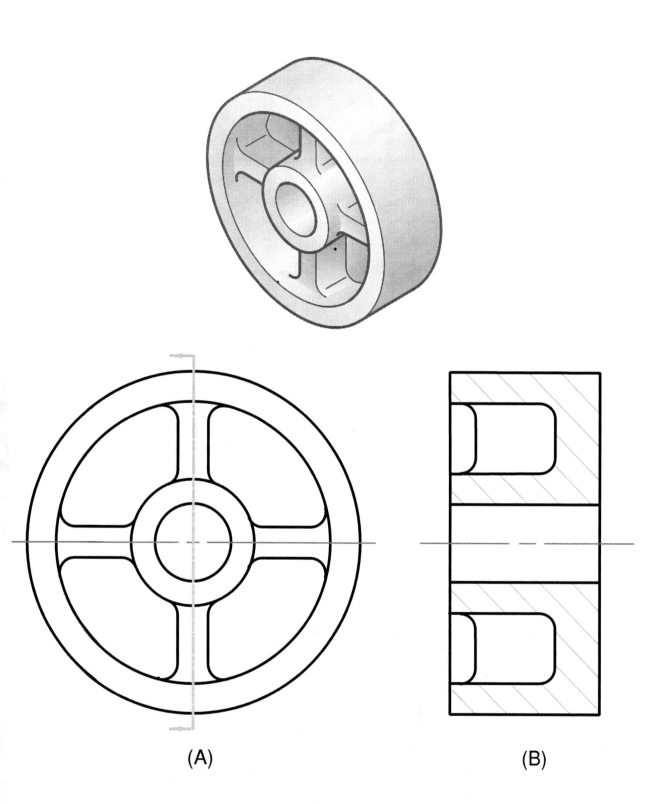

(A)

(B)

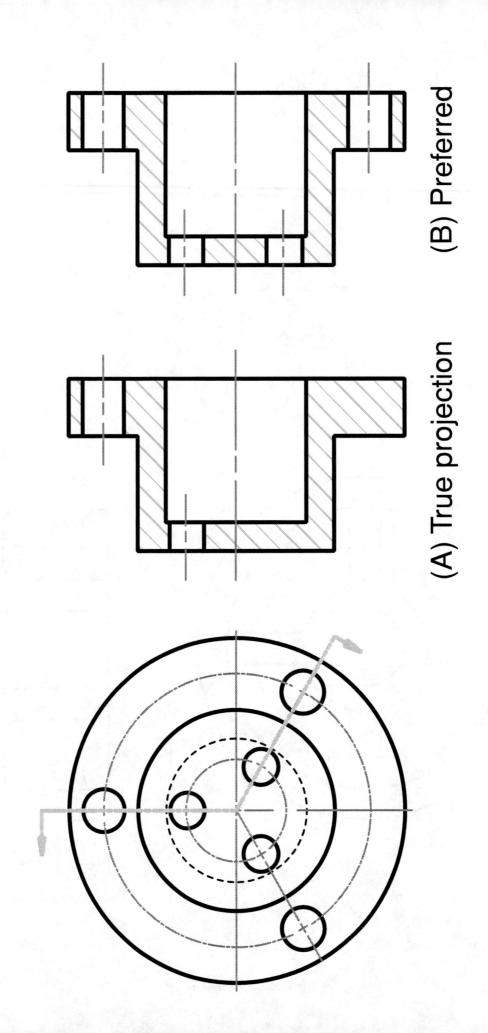

(A) True projection

(B) Preferred

TM-180 Figure 14.45
Aligned Section

TM-181   Figure 14.46
Aligning Spokes

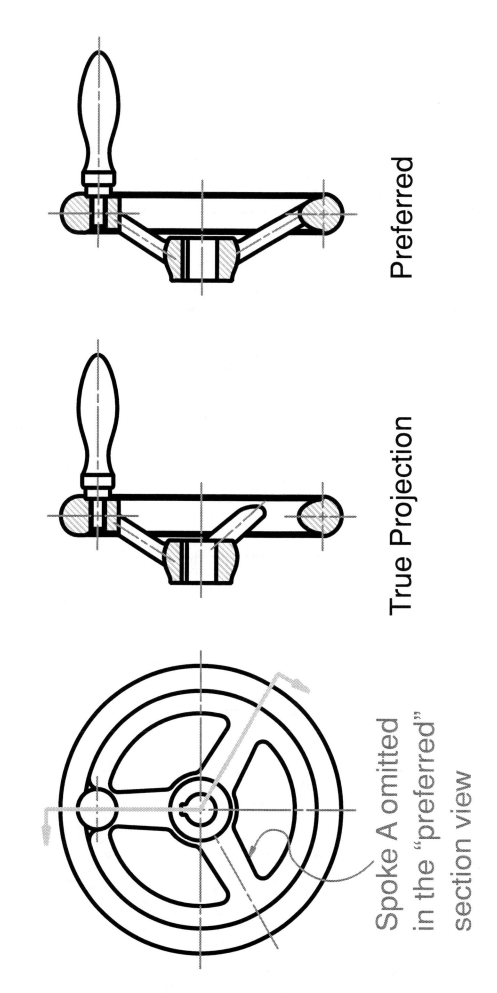

True Projection

Preferred

Spoke A omitted
in the "preferred"
section view

TM-182 Figure 14.47
Aligning Lugs

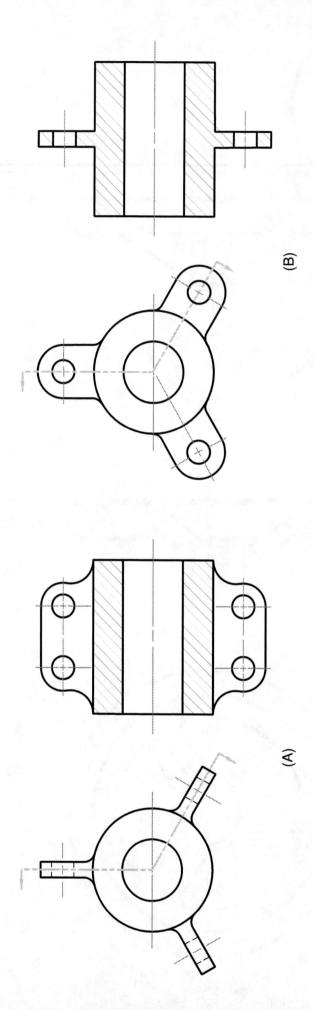

(A)

(B)

TM-183 Figure 14.48
Aligning Ribs

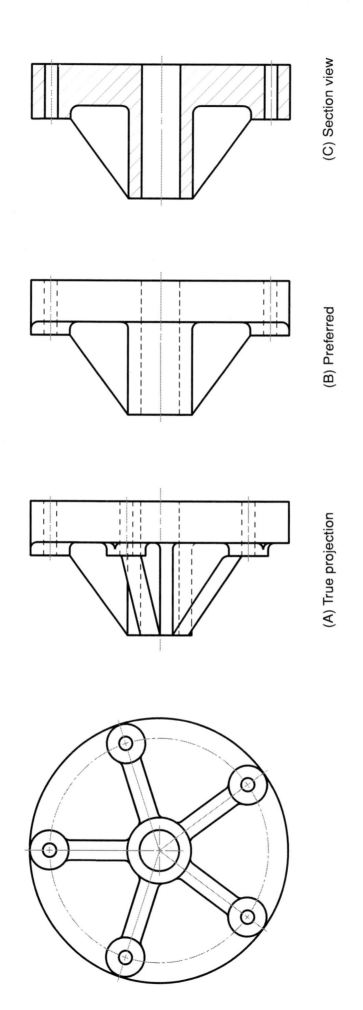

(A) True projection

(B) Preferred

(C) Section view

TM-184 Figure 15.5
Important Elements of a Dimensioned Drawing

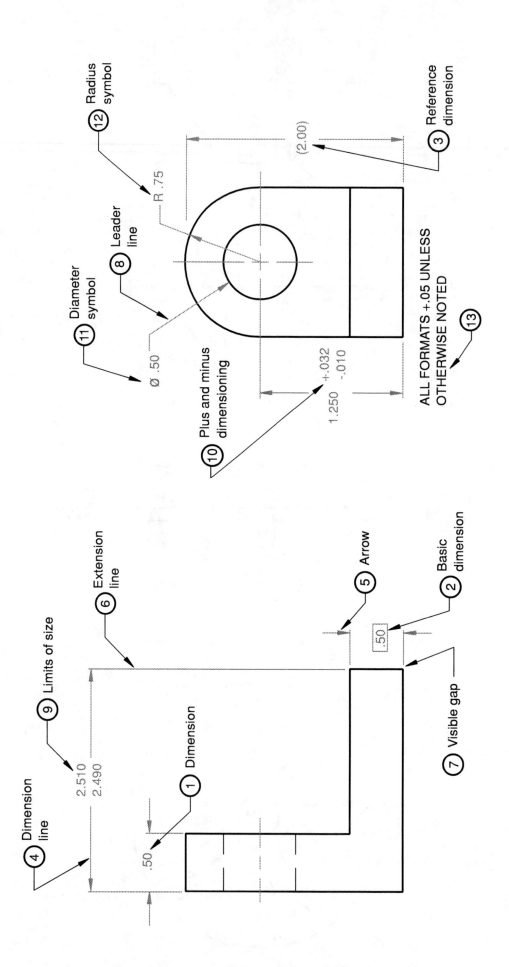

© The McGraw-Hill Companies, Inc., 1997

TM-185   Figure 15.8
Size and location dimensions are used to describe parts for manufacture.

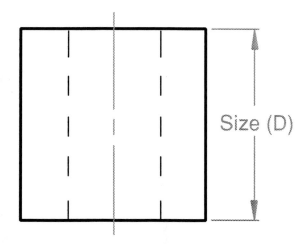

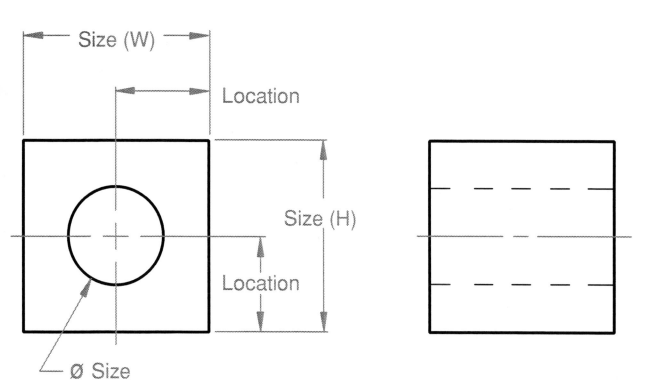

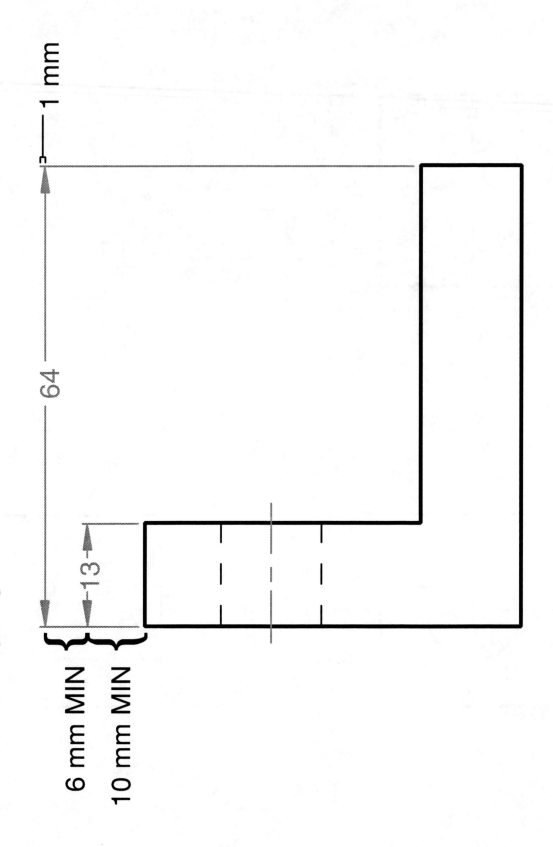

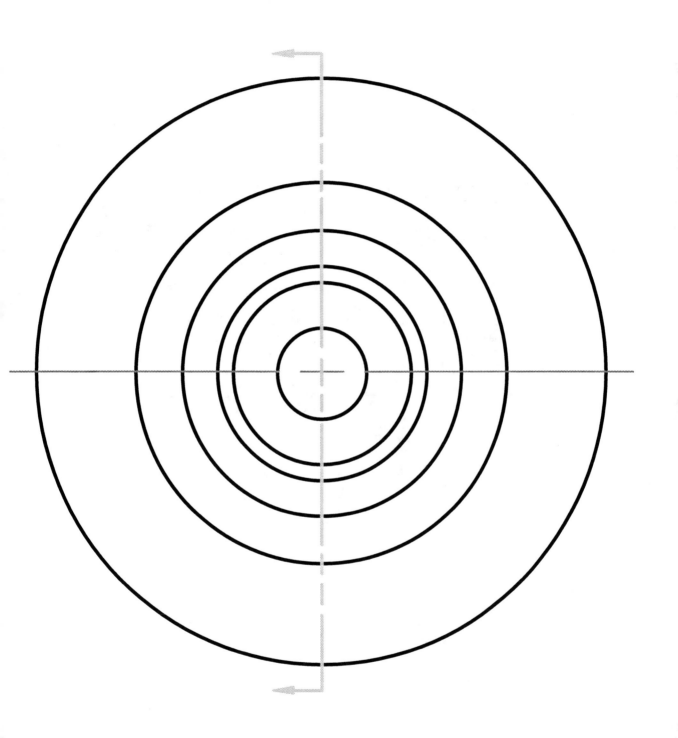

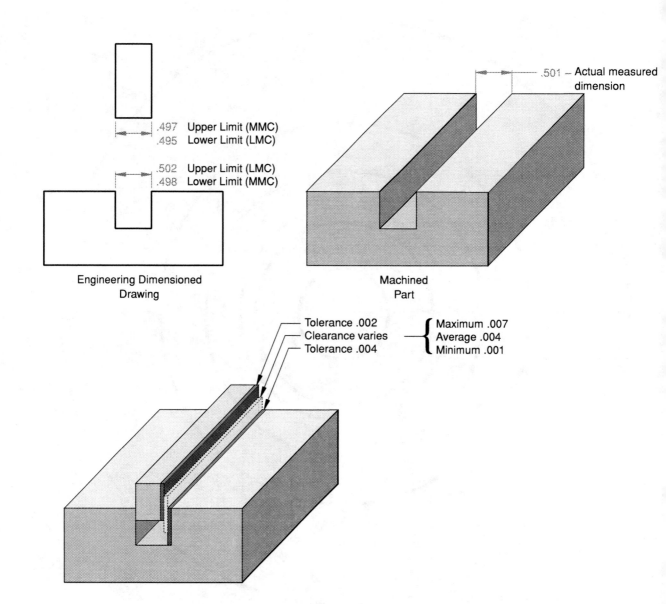

.497 Upper Limit (MMC)
.495 Lower Limit (LMC)

.502 Upper Limit (LMC)
.498 Lower Limit (MMC)

Engineering Dimensioned
Drawing

.501 — Actual measured
dimension

Machined
Part

Tolerance .002
Clearance varies
Tolerance .004

Maximum .007
Average .004
Minimum .001

TM-189   Figure 15.51
Clearance and Interference Fits between Two Shafts and a Hole

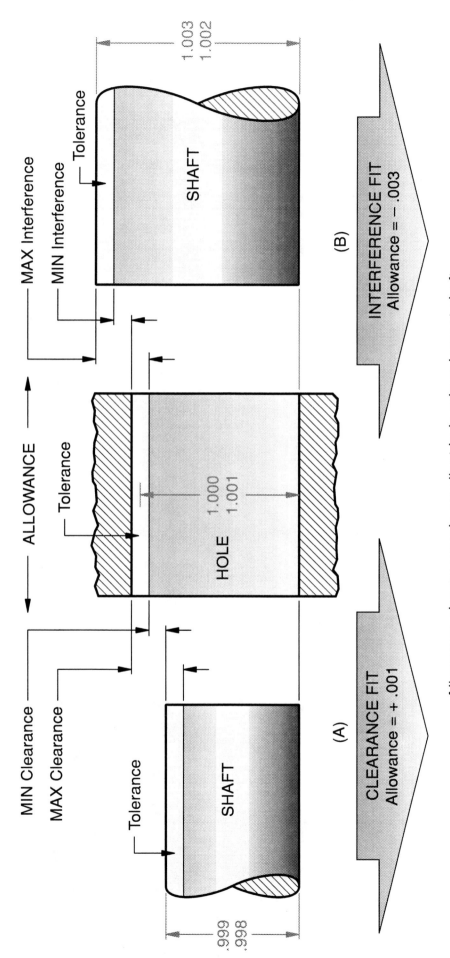

(A) CLEARANCE FIT
Allowance = + .001

(B) INTERFERENCE FIT
Allowance = − .003

Allowance always equals smallest hole minus largest shaft

© The McGraw-Hill Companies, Inc., 1997

TM-190   Figure 15.52
Transition Fit between a Shaft and a Hole

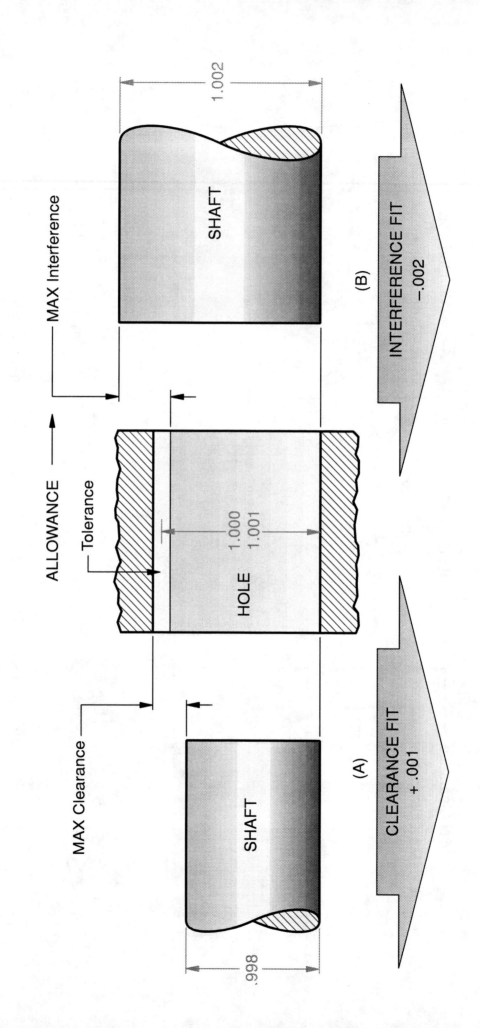

TM-191   Figure 15.60
Important Definitions Used in Metric Tolerancing

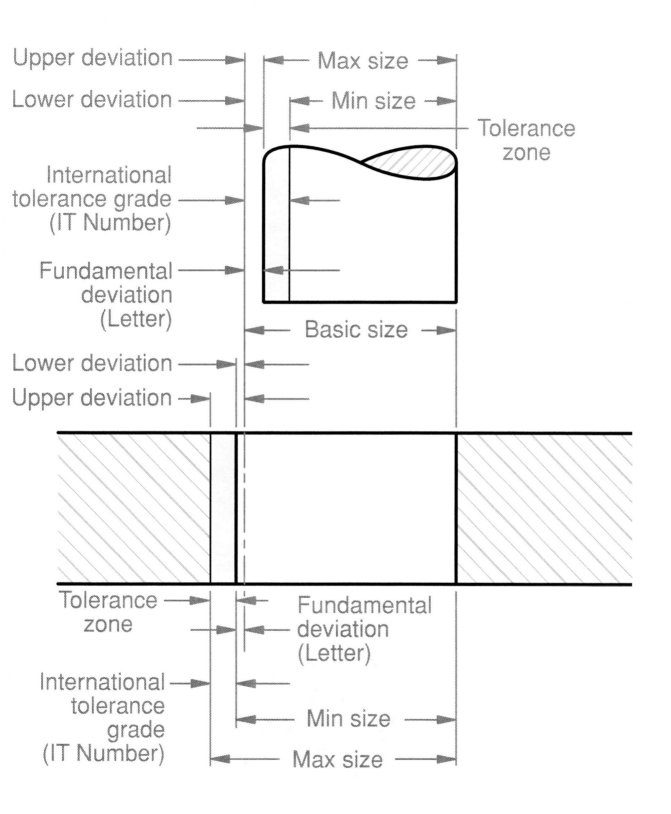

The Line Form and Note Form of Metric Tolerancing

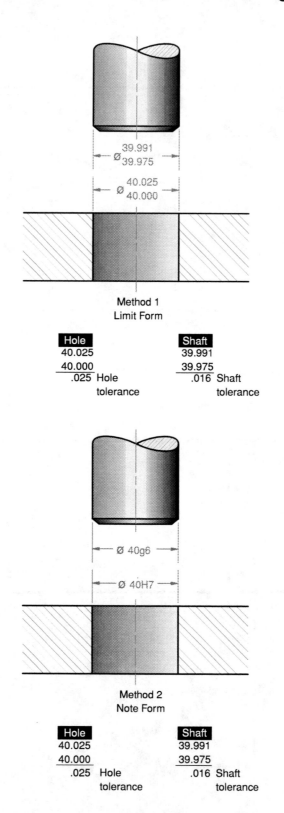

39.991
Ø 39.975

40.025
Ø 40.000

Method 1
Limit Form

Hole	Shaft
40.025	39.991
40.000	39.975
.025 Hole	.016 Shaft
tolerance	tolerance

Ø 40g6

Ø 40H7

Method 2
Note Form

Hole	Shaft
40.025	39.991
40.000	39.975
.025 Hole	.016 Shaft
tolerance	tolerance

TM-193 Figure 15.70
Applying Tolerances for a Clearance Fit Using the Basic Hole System

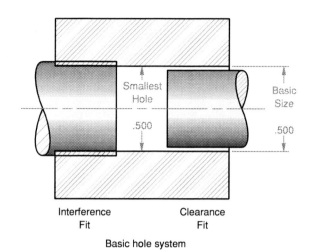

Interference Fit

Clearance Fit

Basic hole system

.500 LOWER LIMIT HOLE

Step 1

```
 .500
-.004  ALLOWANCE
 .496  UPPER LIMIT SHAFT
```

Step 2

```
 .496
-.003  PART TOLERANCE
 .493  LOWER LIMIT SHAFT
```

Step 3

```
 .500
+.003  PART TOLERANCE
 .503  UPPER LIMIT HOLE
```

Step 4

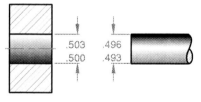

.503   .496
.500   .493

Step 5

```
 .500  SMALLEST HOLE
-.496  LARGEST SHAFT
 .004  Tightest Fit Equals
```

Step 6

```
 .503  LARGEST HOLE
-.493  SMALLEST SHAFT
 .010  Loosest Fit
```

Step 7

```
 .503  UPPER LIMIT HOLE
-.500  LOWER LIMIT HOLE
 .003  PIECE TOLERANCE

 .496  UPPER LIMIT SHAFT
-.493  LOWER LIMIT SHAFT
 .003  PIECE TOLERANCE
```

Step 8

```
 .003  HOLE TOLERANCE
+.003  SHAFT TOLERANCE
 .006  SYSTEM TOLERANCE
```

Step 9

Figure 15.71
Applying Tolerances for an Interference Fit Using the Basic Hole System

.500 LOWER LIMIT HOLE

Step 1

```
 .500
+.007  ALLOWANCE
 .507  UPPER LIMIT SHAFT
```

Step 2

```
 .507
-.003  TOLERANCE
 .504  LOWER LIMIT SHAFT
```

Step 3

```
 .500
+.003  TOLERANCE
 .503  UPPER LIMIT HOLE
```

Step 4

Step 5

```
 .500  SMALLEST HOLE
-.507  LARGEST SHAFT
-.007  Tightest Fit Equals the Allowance
```

Step 6

```
 .503  LARGEST HOLE
-.504  SMALLEST SHAFT
-.001  Loosest Fit
```

Step 7

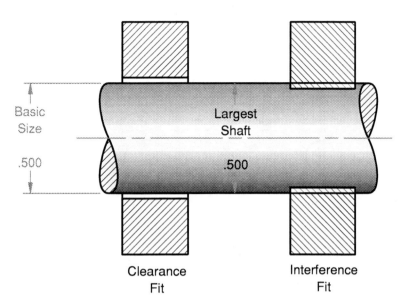

Clearance
Fit

Interference
Fit

Basic shaft system

.500 UPPER LIMIT SHAFT

Step 1

.500
+.004 ALLOWANCE
.504 LOWER LIMIT HOLE

Step 2

.504
+.003 TOLERANCE
.507 UPPER LIMIT HOLE

Step 3

.500
−.003 TOLERANCE
.497 LOWER LIMIT SHAFT

Step 4

TM-196   Figure 16.2
Dimensioning and Tolerancing Symbols

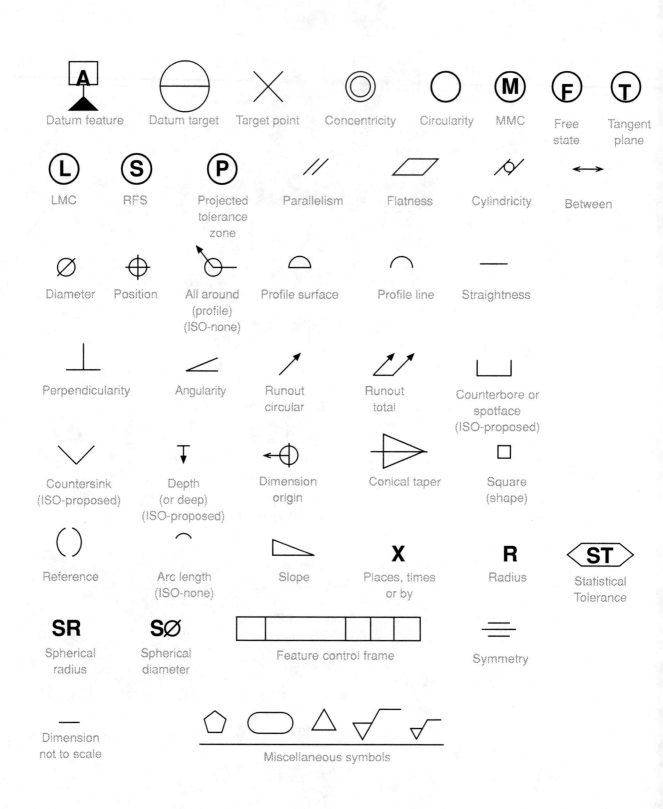

GEOMETRIC TOLERANCING WORKSHEET

PART 1: ISOLATE AND DEFINE THE FUNCTIONS OF THE FEATURE/PART

Basic Function _____

_____

_____

Additional Functions _____

PART 2: PRIORITIZE THE FUNCTIONS

Feature #1 _____ Feature #2 _____ Feature #3 _____

PARTS 3 & 4: CREATE THE DATUM REFERENCE FRAMES & SELECT CONTROLS

Feature # _____ Function _____

Control _____

Primary Datum Feature   Secondary Datum Feature   Tertiary Datum Feature

_____   _____   _____

Feature # _____ Function _____

Control _____

Primary Datum Feature   Secondary Datum Feature   Tertiary Datum Feature

_____   _____   _____

Feature # _____ Function _____

Control _____

Primary Datum Feature   Secondary Datum Feature   Tertiary Datum Feature

_____   _____   _____

PART 5: CALCULATE THE TOLERANCES

Feature # _____ Feature #_____ Feature # _____

Screw Thread Terminology Used with Internal and External Threaded Features

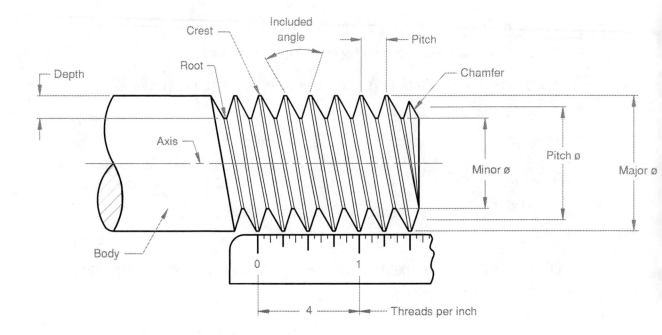

External threads

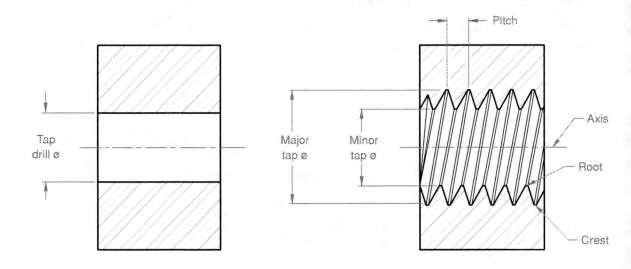

Internal threads

TM-199   Figure 17.6
Standard Thread Note for English Dimension Fasteners

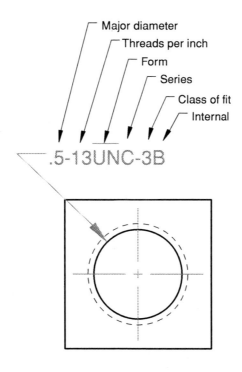

Major diameter
Threads per inch
Form
Series
Class of fit
Internal

.5-13UNC-3B

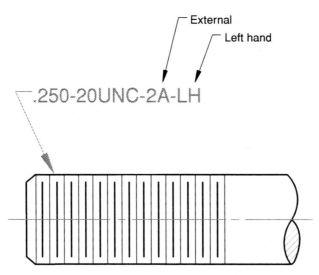

External
Left hand

.250-20UNC-2A-LH

UNC	Means Unified National Coarse
UNF	Means Unified National Fine
UNEF	Means Unified Extra Fine Series
UN	Means Uniform Pitch Series
UNM	Means Unified Miniature Series
NC	Means National Coarse Series
NF	Means National Fine Series
UNR	Means Unified National Round

TM-200   Figure 17.12
Complete Metric Thread Note

Tolerance specified

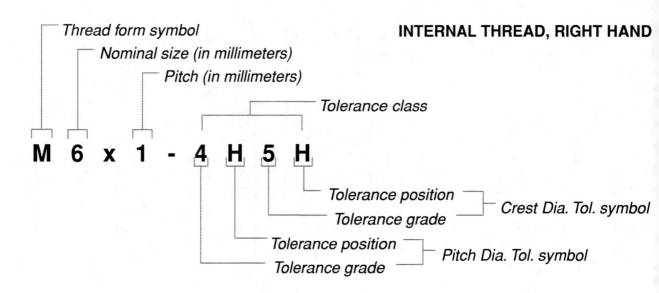

INTERNAL THREAD, RIGHT HAND

Thread form symbol
Nominal size (in millimeters)
Pitch (in millimeters)
Tolerance class

M 6 x 1 - 4 H 5 H

Tolerance position
Crest Dia. Tol. symbol
Tolerance grade
Tolerance position
Pitch Dia. Tol. symbol
Tolerance grade

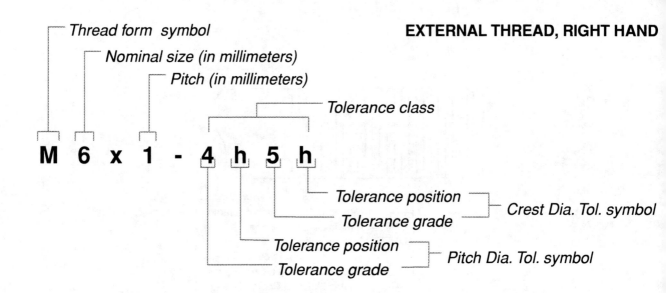

EXTERNAL THREAD, RIGHT HAND

Thread form symbol
Nominal size (in millimeters)
Pitch (in millimeters)
Tolerance class

M 6 x 1 - 4 h 5 h

Tolerance position
Crest Dia. Tol. symbol
Tolerance grade
Tolerance position
Pitch Dia. Tol. symbol
Tolerance grade

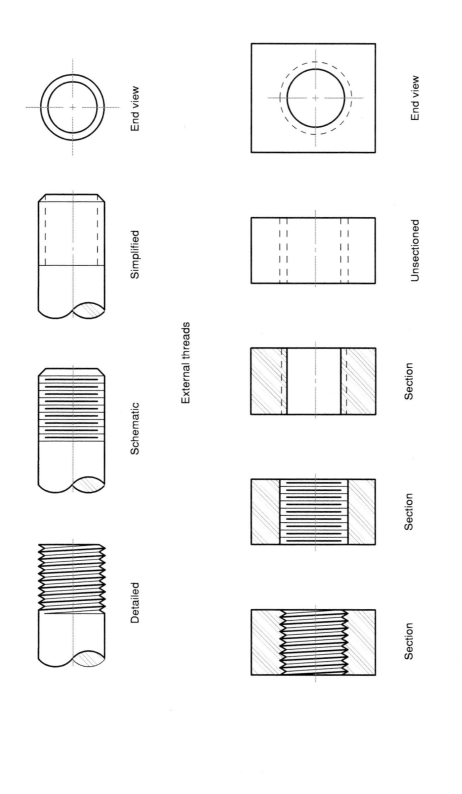

End view

Simplified

Schematic

Detailed

External threads

End view

Unsectioned

Section

Section

Section

Internal threads

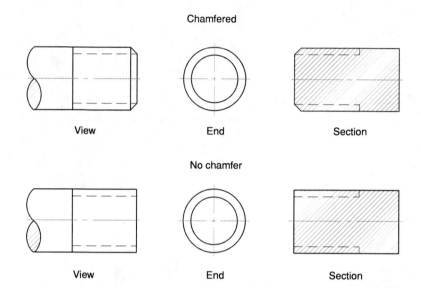

Chamfered

View   End   Section

No chamfer

View   End   Section

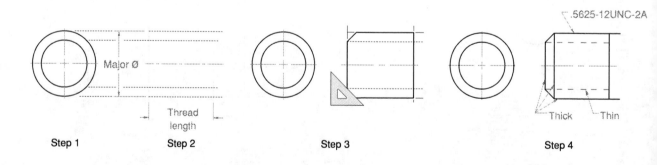

Major Ø

Thread
length

.5625-12UNC-2A

Thick   Thin

Step 1   Step 2   Step 3   Step 4

TM-203 Figure 17.16
Simplified Method of Representing Internal Threads

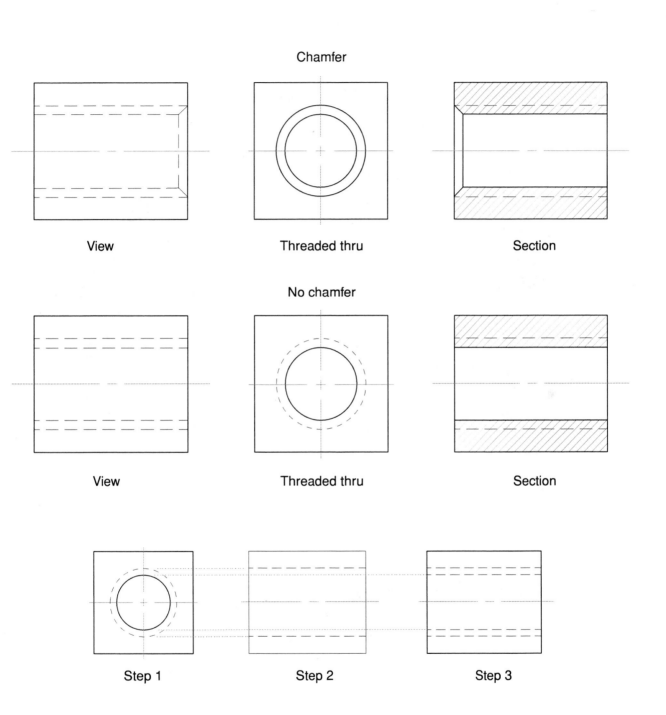

Chamfer

View   Threaded thru   Section

No chamfer

View   Threaded thru   Section

Step 1   Step 2   Step 3

TM-204   Figure 18.12
CIM Model Organization Wheel

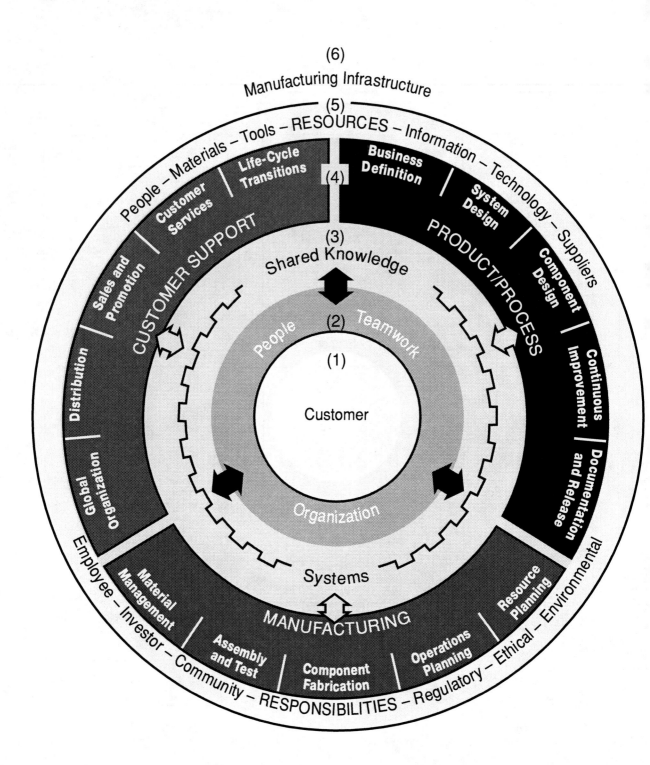

Reprinted courtesy of the Computer and Automated Systems Association (CASA) of the Society of Manufacturing Engineers (SME).

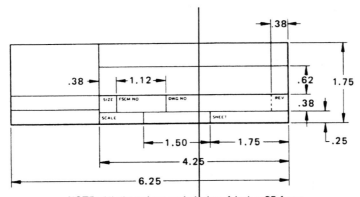

NOTE: All dimensions are in inches. 1 inch = 25.4 mm.
TITLE BLOCK FOR A, B, C, AND G — SIZES

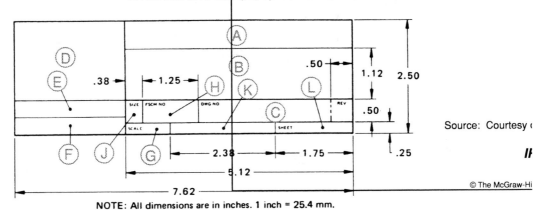

Source: Courtesy

© The McGraw-Hi

NOTE: All dimensions are in inches. 1 inch = 25.4 mm.
TITLE BLOCK FOR D, E, F, H, J, AND K — SIZES

NOTE: All dimensions are in inches. 1 inch = 25.4 mm.
CONTINUATION SHEET TITLE BLOCK FOR A, B, C, and G — SIZES

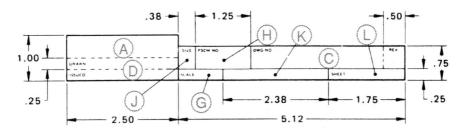

NOTE: All dimensions are in inches. 1 inch = 25.4 mm.
CONTINUATION SHEET TITLE BLOCK FOR D, E, F, H, J, AND K — SIZES

ANSI Y14.1–1980.

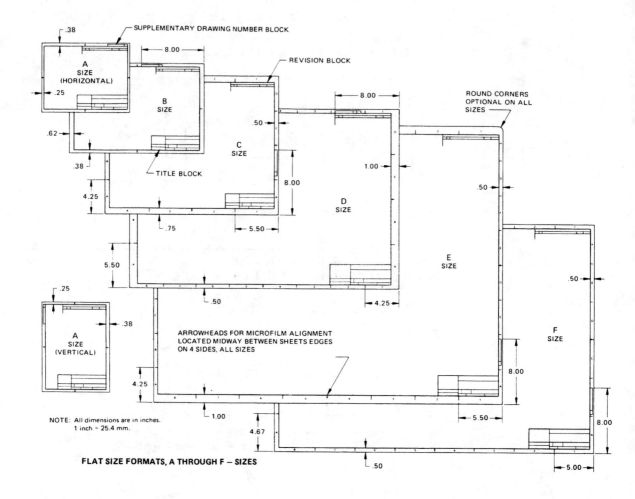

FLAT SIZE FORMATS, A THROUGH F — SIZES

ANSI Y14.1–1980.